INTRODUCING
MATH!
GRADE 8
ARGOPREP

FREE VIDEO EXPLANATIONS

600 QUESTIONS TO PRACTICE

TEACHER RECOMMENDED

TOPICS COVERED
PRACTICE MAKES PERFECT

- The Number System
- Expressions and Equations
- Functions
- Geometry
- Statistics

ArgoPrep is one of the leading providers of supplemental educational products and services. We offer affordable and effective test prep solutions to educators, parents and students. Learning should be fun and easy! For that reason, most of our workbooks come with detailed video answer explanations taught by one of our fabulous instructors.

Our goal is to make your life easier, so let us know how we can help you by e-mailing us at: info@argoprep.com.

Aknowlegments:
Icons made by Freepik, Creaticca Creative Agency, Pixel perfect , Pixel Buddha, Smashicons, Twitter , Good Ware, Smalllikeart, Nikita Golubev, monkik, DinosoftLabs, Icon Pond from www.flaticon.com

ArgoPrep is a recipient of the prestigious **Mom's Choice Award**.

ArgoPrep also received the 2019 **Seal of Approval** from Homeschool.com for our award-winning workbooks.

ArgoPrep was awarded the 2019 **National Parenting Products Award** and a **Gold Medal Parent's Choice Award**.

Want an amazing offer from ArgoPrep?

7 DAY
ACCESS

to our online premium content at **www.argoprep.com**

Online premium content includes practice quizzes and drills with video explanations and an automatic grading system.

Chat with us live at **www. argoprep.com** for this exclusive offer.

ARGOPREP

TABLE OF CONTENTS

Chapter 1 - The Number System 10

1.1.A Irrational Numbers. 12

1.1.B Approximating Irrational Numbers 17

1.2. Chapter Test 22

Chapter 2 - Expressions & Equations **26**

2.1.A Properties of Exponents. 28

2.1.B Square Roots. 32

2.1.C Powers of Ten. 36

2.1.D Performing Operations with Scientific Notation 42

2.2.A Graphing Proportional Relationships .46

2.2.B Determining Y-Intercepts and Explaining Slope 58

2.3.A Solving Linear Equations 67

2.3.B Solving Pairs of Linear Equations 72

2.4. Chapter Test 80

Chapter 3 - Functions **86**

3.1.A Intro to Functions. 88

3.1.B Comparing Functions. 97

3.1.C Nonlinear Functions. 106

3.2.A Constructing Functions 113

3.2.B Analyzing Functional Relationships .121

3.3. Chapter Test 130

Chapter 4 - Geometry **138**

4.1.A Experimenting with Rotations, Reflections and Translations. 140

4.1.B Congruent Figures. 150

4.1.C Transformations on a Coordinate Plane 158

4.1.D Similar Figures. 168

4.2.A Intro to Pythagorean Theorem 176

4.2.B Applying the Pythagorean Theorem - Part I. 181

4.2.C Applying the Pythagorean Theorem - Part II 185

4.3 Volume of Cones, Cylinders and Spheres. 192

4.4. Chapter Test 197

Chapter 5 - Statistics **206**

5.1.A Scatter Plots 208

5.1.B Linear Associations 220

5.1.C Equation of a Linear Model. 228

5.1.D Two Way Models 238

5.1. Chapter Test 246

Chapter 6 - Mixed Assessment **254**

Answer Key **290**

HOW TO USE THE BOOK

Welcome to the Introducing Math! series by ArgoPrep.

This workbook is designed to provide you with a comprehensive overview of Grade 8 mathematics.

While working through this workbook, be sure to read the topic overview that will give you a general foundation of the concept. At the end of each chapter, there is a chapter test that will assess how well you understood the topics presented.

This workbook comes with free digital video explanations that you can access on our website. If you are unsure on how to answer a question, we strongly recommend watching the video explanations as it will reinforce the fundamental concepts.

We strive to provide you with an amazing learning experience. If you have any suggestions or need further assistance, don't hesitate to email us at info@argoprep.com or chat with us live on our website at www.argoprep.com

HOW TO WATCH VIDEO EXPLANATIONS
IT IS ABSOLUTELY FREE

Download our app:
ArgoPrep Video Explanations
to access videos on any mobile device or tablet.

OR

Step 1 - Visit our website at: www.argoprep.com/k8
Step 2 - Click on JOIN FOR FREE button located on the top right corner.
Step 3 - Choose the grade level workbook you have.
Step 4 - Sign up as a Learner, Parent or a Teacher.
Step 5 - Register using your email or social networks.
Step 6 - From your dashboard cick on FREE WORKBOOKS EXPLANATION on the left and choose the workbook you have.

OTHER BOOKS BY ARGOPREP

Here are some other test prep workbooks by ArgoPrep you may be interested in. All of our workbooks come equipped with detailed video explanations to make your learning experience a breeze! Visit us at **www.argoprep.com**

COMMON CORE MATH SERIES

COMMON CORE ELA SERIES

INTRODUCING MATH!

Introducing Math! by ArgoPrep is an award-winning series created by certified teachers to provide students with high-quality practice problems. Our workbooks include topic overviews with instruction, practice questions, answer explanations along with digital access to video explanations. Practice in confidence - with ArgoPrep!

   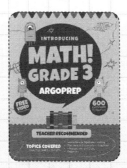 

YOGA MINDFULNESS FOR KIDS

HIGHER LEVEL EXAMS

KIDS SUMMER ACADEMY SERIES

ArgoPrep's **Kids Summer Academy** series helps prevent summer learning loss and gets students ready for their new school year by reinforcing core foundations in math, english and science. Our workbooks also introduce new concepts so students can get a head start and be on top of their game for the new school year!

Meet the ArgoPrep heroes.

Are you ready to go on an incredible adventure and complete your journey with them to become a **SUPER** student?

WATER FIRE

MYSTICAL NINJA

GREEN POISON

FIRESTORM WARRIOR

RAPID NINJA

CAPTAIN ARGO

THUNDER WARRIOR

ADRASTOS THE SUPER WARRIOR

Our **Kids Summer Academy** series by **ArgoPrep** is designed to keep students engaged with fun graphics and activities. Our curriculum is aligned with state standards to help your child prepare for their new school year.

Chapter 1:
The Number System

1.1.A. Irrational Numbers page 12

1.1.B. Approximating Irrational Numbers page 17

1.2. Chapter Test page 22

A rational number is any number that can be expressed as a fraction of two integers. For example...

.22222.. (repeating 2) is a rational number. Even though the decimal is infinite, it repeats. It can be expressed as the simple fraction $\frac{2}{9}$

An irrational number cannot be expressed as a simple fraction. Irrational numbers have infinite decimal expansions in which the numbers do not repeat. For example...

Pi (π) is an irrational number because the decimal continues infinitely without a patern.

$\sqrt{2}$ is an irrational number because the decimal continues infinitely without a pattern.

Practice Questions

Determine whether numbers are rational or irrational for questions 1 – 15

1. 2π

   A. rational

   SHOW YOUR WORK

   B. irrational

2. 0.125

   A. rational

   SHOW YOUR WORK

   B. irrational

3. **0.3333333$\overline{3}$ (3 repeating)**

A. rational

B. irrational

 SHOW YOUR WORK

4. $\sqrt{3}$

A. rational

B. irrational

SHOW YOUR WORK

5. 1.5

A. rational

B. irrational

SHOW YOUR WORK

6. $\sqrt{4}$

A. rational

B. irrational

SHOW YOUR WORK

7. $\frac{1}{2}$

A. rational

B. irrational

SHOW YOUR WORK

8. $\sqrt{99}$

   A. rational

   B. irrational

SHOW YOUR WORK

9. -3

   A. rational

   B. irrational

SHOW YOUR WORK

10. $\sqrt{\dfrac{3}{2}}$

   A. rational

   B. irrational

SHOW YOUR WORK

11. $\dfrac{3}{2}$

   A. rational

   B. irrational

SHOW YOUR WORK

12. 5π

   A. rational

   B. irrational

SHOW YOUR WORK

13. -1.52

   A. rational

   B. irrational

SHOW YOUR WORK

14. 51,234

A. rational

B. irrational

SHOW YOUR WORK

15. 0

A. rational

B. irrational

SHOW YOUR WORK

Classify the numbers below. Select <u>all</u> that apply.

16. -2

A. rational

B. irrational

C. integer

D. whole number

SHOW YOUR WORK

17. 4π

A. rational

B. irrational

C. integer

D. whole number

SHOW YOUR WORK

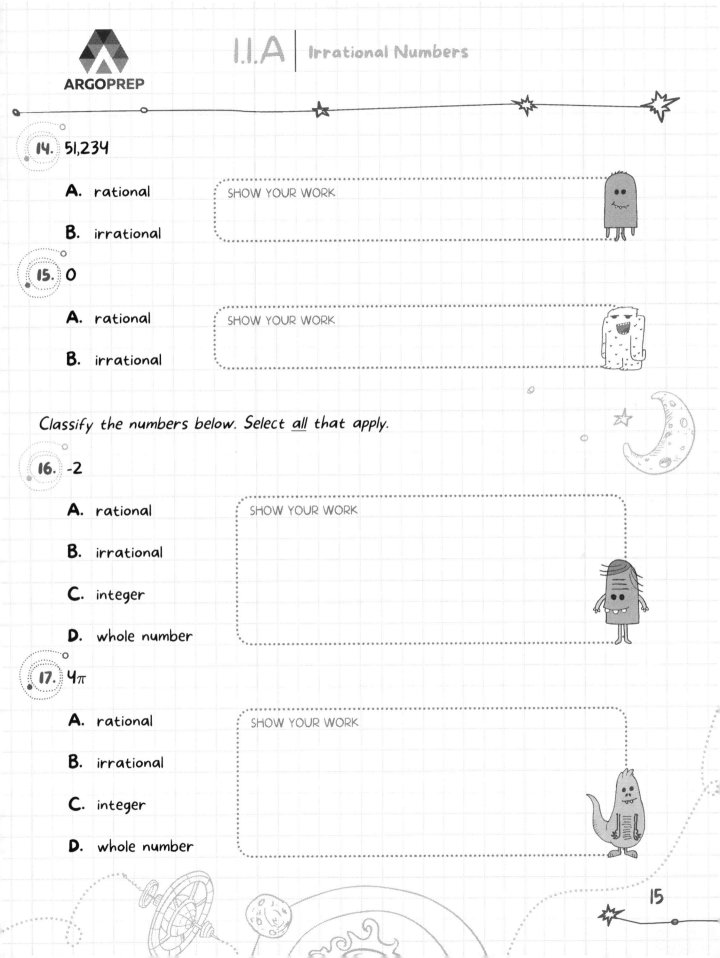

18. $\dfrac{5}{6}$

A. rational

B. irrational

C. integer

D. whole number

SHOW YOUR WORK

19. $-\sqrt{36}$

A. rational

B. irrational

C. integer

D. whole number

SHOW YOUR WORK

20. 0

A. rational

B. irrational

C. integer

D. whole number

SHOW YOUR WORK

ARGOPREP

There are times when we need to approximate irrational numbers in order to solve problems. For example...

Plot $\sqrt{2}$ on the number line below.

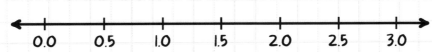

In order to plot the number, we need to convert it into a value that fits on a number line.

Step 1: Determine the closest rational, whole number

We know that the square root of **2** is somewhere between 1 and 2 because the $\sqrt{1}$ is 1 and the $\sqrt{4}$ is **2**.

$$1 < \sqrt{2} < 2$$

Step 2: Check Squares

We can try to get a more approximate estimation by checking the squares of numbers in between 1 and **2**. Let's start with 1.5 since it's in the middle.

$$1.5^2 = 2.25$$

So, $\sqrt{2.25} = 1.5$. Therefore, $1 < \sqrt{2} < 1.5$

Now we know that $\sqrt{2}$ is greater than 1 but less than 1.5. Let's try going down one more number.

$$1.4^2 = 1.96$$

So, $\sqrt{1.96} = 1.4$

Now we know that $\sqrt{2}$ is greater than 1.4 but less than 1.5.

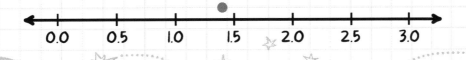

Practice Questions

Use the number line below to answer questions 1 - 6

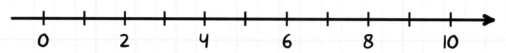

1. Plot π on the number line

SHOW YOUR WORK

2. Plot √11 on the number line

SHOW YOUR WORK

3. Plot √3 on the number line

SHOW YOUR WORK

4. Plot 3π on the number line

SHOW YOUR WORK

5. Plot $\frac{1}{2}\pi$ on the number line

SHOW YOUR WORK

6. Plot $\sqrt{50}$ on the number line

SHOW YOUR WORK

7. Order the numbers below from least to greatest without using a calculator

4, 5, -4, $\sqrt{24}$

SHOW YOUR WORK

8. Order the numbers below from least to greatest without using a calculator

$\frac{5}{2}$, π, 3, 4

SHOW YOUR WORK

9. Order the numbers below from least to greatest without using a calculator

3, 4, $\sqrt{10}$

SHOW YOUR WORK

10. Order the numbers below from least to greatest without using a calculator

3, $\sqrt{14}$, 5, 4

SHOW YOUR WORK

11. Order the numbers below from least to greatest without using a calculator

SHOW YOUR WORK

2π, 6, 3, 1

12. Order the numbers below from least to greatest without using a calculator

SHOW YOUR WORK

$\frac{1}{2}\pi$, 1, 2, 3

13. Use whole numbers to create an inequality for the irrational number

.... $< \pi - 2 <$ ....

SHOW YOUR WORK

14. Use whole numbers to create an inequality for the irrational number

.... $< \sqrt{83} <$ ....

SHOW YOUR WORK

15. Use whole numbers to create an inequality for the irrational number

.... $< 12\pi <$ ....

SHOW YOUR WORK

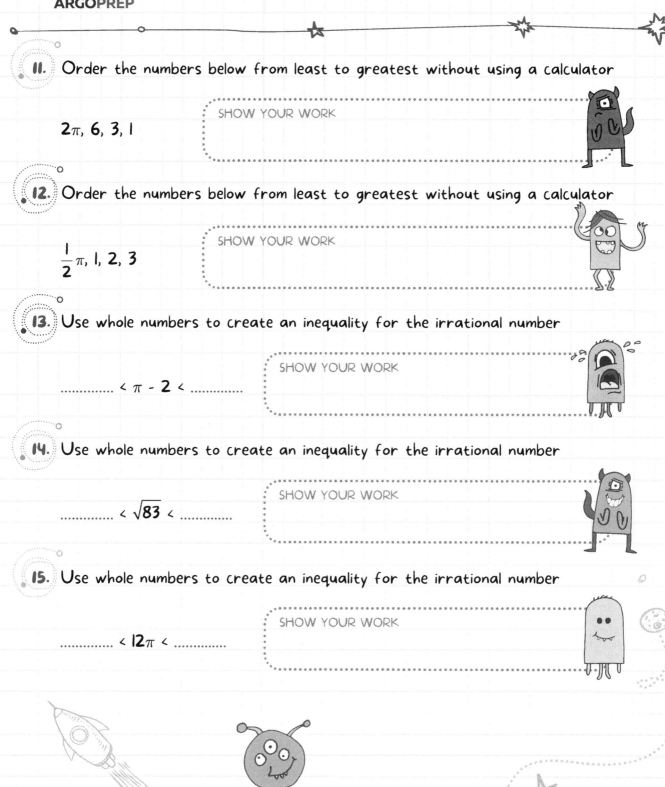

16. Use whole numbers to create an inequality for the irrational number

.... < $\sqrt{75}$ < ....

SHOW YOUR WORK

17. Use whole numbers to create an inequality for the irrational number

.... < $\sqrt{5}$ < ....

SHOW YOUR WORK

18. Estimate $\sqrt[3]{5}$ to the tenth.

SHOW YOUR WORK

19. Estimate $\sqrt{6}$ to the tenth.

SHOW YOUR WORK

20. Estimate $2\pi \times 3$ to the nearest whole number.

SHOW YOUR WORK

Determine whether numbers are rational or irrational for questions 1 – 10

1. π

A. rational

B. irrational

SHOW YOUR WORK

2. 0.75

A. rational

B. irrational

SHOW YOUR WORK

3. $\dfrac{\pi}{2}$

A. rational

B. irrational

SHOW YOUR WORK

4. -2

A. rational

B. irrational

SHOW YOUR WORK

5. $\sqrt{9}$

A. rational

B. irrational

SHOW YOUR WORK

6. .44444444...(repeating 4)

A. rational

SHOW YOUR WORK

B. irrational

7. $\sqrt[3]{5}$

A. rational

SHOW YOUR WORK

B. irrational

8. $\frac{1}{2}$

A. rational

SHOW YOUR WORK

B. irrational

9. $\sqrt{111}$

A. rational

SHOW YOUR WORK

B. irrational

10. $\sqrt{81}$

A. rational

SHOW YOUR WORK

B. irrational

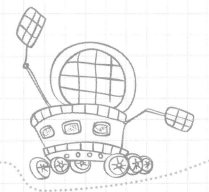

ARGOPREP

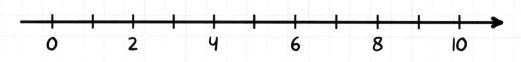

Use the number line below to answer questions 11 - 14

$$\xleftarrow{\hspace{0.5cm}}\overset{\displaystyle 0 \quad\quad 2 \quad\quad 4 \quad\quad 6 \quad\quad 8 \quad\quad 10}{\underset{|\;|\;|\;|\;|\;|\;|\;|\;|\;|\;|\;}{\hspace{6cm}}}\xrightarrow{\hspace{0.5cm}}$$

11. Plot $4\pi - 10$ on the number line

SHOW YOUR WORK

12. Plot $\sqrt{12}$ on the number line

SHOW YOUR WORK

13. Plot $\frac{1}{3}\pi$ on the number line

SHOW YOUR WORK

14. Round $6\pi - 1$ to the nearest whole number

SHOW YOUR WORK

15. Round $\frac{\pi}{3}$ to the nearest whole number

SHOW YOUR WORK

16. Round $2\pi + 6$ to the nearest whole number

SHOW YOUR WORK

17. Order the numbers below from least to greatest without using a calculator

$\sqrt{112}$, 11, 9 10

SHOW YOUR WORK

18. Order the numbers below from least to greatest without using a calculator

$\sqrt{24}$, 5, 4

SHOW YOUR WORK

19. Order the numbers below from least to greatest without using a calculator

$\sqrt{8}$, 3, 4

SHOW YOUR WORK

20. Order the numbers below from least to greatest without using a calculator

$\sqrt{34}$, 5, 6

SHOW YOUR WORK

Chapter 2:
Expressions & Equations

2.1.A. Properties of Exponents page 28

2.1.B. Square Roots page 32

2.1.C. Powers of Ten page 36

2.1.D. Performing Operations with Scientific Notation page 42

2.2.A. Graphing Proportional Relationships page 46

2.2.B. Determining Y-Intercepts and Explaining Slope page 58

2.3A. Solving Linear Equations page 67

2.3B. Solving Pairs of Linear Equations page 72

2.4. Chapter Test page 80

ARGOPREP
STUDY SMARTER, NOT HARDER

Exponent properties are different than integer properties. The chart below shows how you can generate equivalent expressions when there is more than one exponent.

Properties of Exponents

Multiplication	Division
$3^4 \times 3^2 = \text{............}$	$\dfrac{3^4}{3^2} = \text{............}$
If two exponents have the same base, you add them.	If two exponents have the same base, you subtract them.
$3^{4+2} = 3^6$	$3^{4-2} = 3^2$
Negative Exponents	**Negative Integers**
	-3^2
	If the base has a negative sign outside of parenthesis, solve the exponent as a positive base then add the negative sign to the solution.
3^{-2}	$3 \times 3 = -9$
If the exponent is negative, the base becomes inverse and the exponent becomes positive.	$(-3)^2$
$\dfrac{1}{3^2} = \dfrac{1}{9}$	If the base has a negative sign inside of parenthesis, solve the exponent using the negative base. Two negatives make a positive.
	$-3 \times -3 = 9$

Practice Questions

1. $(-2)^4 + 1 =$ ....

> SHOW YOUR WORK

2. $5^{-2} =$ ....

> SHOW YOUR WORK

3. $(3^2)(4^2) =$ ....

> SHOW YOUR WORK

4. $\dfrac{5^6}{5^4} =$ ....

> SHOW YOUR WORK

5. $-6^2 =$ ....

> SHOW YOUR WORK

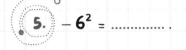

6. $4^3 \times 4$ = ...

SHOW YOUR WORK

7. $3^4 + (-3)^4$ = ...

SHOW YOUR WORK

8. 12^{-2} = ...

SHOW YOUR WORK

9. $\dfrac{8^2}{8^3}$ = ...

SHOW YOUR WORK

10. $\left(\dfrac{1}{2}\right)^{-2}$ = ...

SHOW YOUR WORK

11. $(-3)^4$ = ...

SHOW YOUR WORK

12. $\dfrac{2^2 \times 2^6}{2^5} = $ ....

SHOW YOUR WORK

13. $25^3 \times 25^{-3} = $ ....

SHOW YOUR WORK

14. $5^0 = $ ....

SHOW YOUR WORK

15. $(-5)^3 = $ ....

SHOW YOUR WORK

A **square root** ($\sqrt{}$) is the value that a number has when it is multiplied by itself. Every square root has a positive and negative value.

$$\sqrt{x^2} = \pm x$$

For example...

$$\sqrt{16} = ?$$

It could be:

$$\sqrt{16} = +4 \qquad \text{because } 4 \times 4 = 16$$

It could also be:

$$\sqrt{16} = -4 \qquad \text{because } -4 \times -4 = 16$$

Therefore:

$$\sqrt{16} = \pm 4$$

A **cube root** ($\sqrt[3]{}$) is the value that a number has when cubed. It only has one outcome.

$$\sqrt[3]{x^3} = x$$

For example...

$$\sqrt[3]{8} = ?$$

We know that $2^3 = 8$

So, $\sqrt[3]{8} = 2$

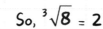

Practice Questions

1. $\sqrt{64}$ = ...

SHOW YOUR WORK

2. $\sqrt{36}$ = ...

SHOW YOUR WORK

3. $\sqrt{121}$ = ...

SHOW YOUR WORK

4. $\sqrt{9}$ = ...

SHOW YOUR WORK

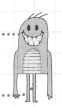

5. $\sqrt{25}$ = ...

SHOW YOUR WORK

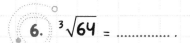

6. $\sqrt[3]{64}$ = ...

SHOW YOUR WORK

7. $\sqrt[3]{343}$ = ...

SHOW YOUR WORK

8. $\sqrt[3]{125}$ = ...

SHOW YOUR WORK

9. $\sqrt[3]{27}$ = ...

SHOW YOUR WORK

10. $\sqrt[3]{1000}$ = ...

SHOW YOUR WORK

11. $\sqrt{x}$ = 9. Solve for x

SHOW YOUR WORK

12. $\sqrt{x} = 7$. Solve for x

SHOW YOUR WORK

13. $\sqrt{x} = 10$. Solve for x

SHOW YOUR WORK

14. $\sqrt[3]{x} = 9$. Solve for x

SHOW YOUR WORK

15. $\sqrt[3]{x} = 12$. Solve for x

SHOW YOUR WORK

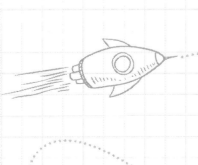

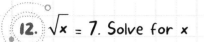

We can use what we know about exponent properties to estimate very large or very small numbers.

For example...

Johnny's tower is **8,000,013** inches tall. Mac's tower is **42** inches tall. How large is Johnny's tower compared to Mac's tower?

Step 1: Rewrite the height of Johnny's tower using **scientific notation.**

Approximate 8,000,013 by rounding to 8,000,000

8,000,000 can be rewritten as 8×10^6 because the decimal is six places to the right.

$$8 \times 10^6$$

Step 2: Rewrite the height of Mac's tower using **scientific notation.**

Approximate to 42 by rounding to 40

40 can be rewritten as 4×10^1 using scientific notation because the decimal is one place to the right.

$$4 \times 10^1$$

Step 3: Compare the two sizes using division.

We need to divide in order to approximate how many times larger Johnny's tower is than Mac's tower.

$$\frac{8 \times 10^6}{4 \times 10^1} = \frac{8}{4} \times \frac{10^6}{10^1}$$

Remember that exponents are subtracted in division problems.

$$2 \times 10^{6-1=5}$$

$$2 \times 10^5$$

Johnny's tower is **200,000** times larger than Mac's tower.

Step 4: Check your answer.

You can check you answer with multiplication

$$40 \times 200,000 = 8,000,000 \checkmark$$

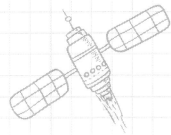

Practice Questions

1. $4 \times 10^7 =$ ....

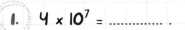
SHOW YOUR WORK

2. $5 \times 10^{-2} =$ ....

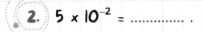
SHOW YOUR WORK

3. $10 \times 10^{10} = $ ....

SHOW YOUR WORK

4. $6 \times 10^x = .06$. Solve for x.

SHOW YOUR WORK

5. $2 \times 10^x = 2{,}000$. Solve for x.

SHOW YOUR WORK

6. $8 \times 10^x = 80$. Solve for x.

SHOW YOUR WORK

7. 2×10^7 is .... times as large as 1×10^1

A. 2,000

B. 20,000

C. 200,000

D. 2,000,000

SHOW YOUR WORK

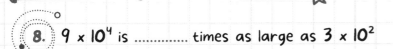

8. 9×10^4 is .... times as large as 3×10^2

A. 3

B. 30

C. 300

D. 3,000

SHOW YOUR WORK

9. 6×10^4 is .... times as large as 2×10^3

A. 3

B. 30

C. 300

D. 3000

SHOW YOUR WORK

Use the scenario below to answer questions 10 – 12

The large container holds **3210** ounces. The small container holds .1 ounces.

10. Which of the following is the best approximation for the volume of the large container?

A. 3×10^3

B. 3×10^4

SHOW YOUR WORK

11. Which of the following is the best approximation for the volume of the small container?

A. 1×10^{-1}

B. 1×10^{-2}

SHOW YOUR WORK

12. The volume of the large container is approximately .... times as large as the volume of the small container.

A. 3

B. 300

C. 3000

D. 30,000

SHOW YOUR WORK

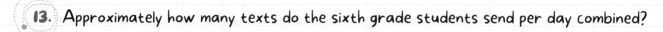

Use the scenario below to answer questions 13 – 15

The sixth grade students send **20,071** texts per day combined. The eighth grade students send **8,002,102** texts per day combined.

13. Approximately how many texts do the sixth grade students send per day combined?

A. 2×10^{3}

B. 2×10^{4}

SHOW YOUR WORK

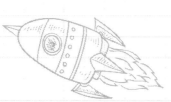

14. Approximately how many texts do the eighth grade students send per day combined?

A. 8×10^5

B. 8×10^6

SHOW YOUR WORK

15. Approximately how many times more texts do the eighth grade students send?

A. 4

B. 40

C. 400

D. 4000

SHOW YOUR WORK

We can use exponent properties to solve equations involving scientific notation.

For example...

$$8.2 \times 10^4 + 3.1 \times 10^3 = \ldots\ldots\ldots$$

When adding and subtracting, we can only simplify powers that are equal.

$x^2 + x^2 = 2x^2$ This expression can be simplified because the exponents are equivalent

$x^2 + x^3$ This expression cannot be simplified

In order to solve the example problem, we need to rewrite the expression so that the exponents are equivalent.

$$8.2 \times 10^4 + 3.1 \times 10^3 = \ldots\ldots\ldots$$

We can rewrite 8.2×10^4 as 82.0×10^3 by moving the decimal to the right one space.

$$82.0 \times 10^3 + 3.1 \times 10^3$$

Now we can add the two values.

$$85.1 \times 10^3$$

We still need to simplify the answer.

$$8.51 \times 10^4 \text{ or } 85,100$$

We can check our answer by writing the values out in numerical form.

$$8.2 \times 10^4 = 82,000$$
$$3.1 \times 10^3 = 3,100$$
$$82,000 + 3,100 = 85,100$$

$$8.51 \times 10^4 \checkmark$$

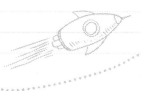

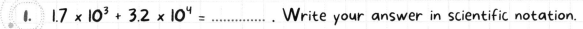

Practice Questions

1. $1.7 \times 10^3 + 3.2 \times 10^4 =$ .... Write your answer in scientific notation.

SHOW YOUR WORK

2. $2.63 \times 10^{-1} + 4.6 \times 10^{-2} =$ .... Write your answer in scientific notation.

SHOW YOUR WORK

3. $6.8 \times 10^6 + 230,000 =$ .... Write your answer in scientific notation.

SHOW YOUR WORK

4. $5.4 \times 10^{-2} + 4.3 \times 10^{-1} =$ .... Write your answer in scientific notation.

SHOW YOUR WORK

5. $520 - 1.0 \times 10^2 =$ .... Write your answer in scientific notation.

SHOW YOUR WORK

6. $6.3 \times 10^4 - 1.5 \times 10^3 =$ .... Write your answer in scientific notation.

SHOW YOUR WORK

7. $27,000 - 7.2 \times 10^3 =$ .... Write your answer in scientific notation.

SHOW YOUR WORK

8. $(1.1 \times 10^2) \times (3.4 \times 10^4) =$ .... Write your answer in scientific notation.

SHOW YOUR WORK

9. $1,200 \times (3.4 \times 10^{-2}) =$ .... Write your answer in scientific notation.

SHOW YOUR WORK

10. $(6.2 \times 10^5) \times (4.2 \times 10^2) =$ .... Write your answer in scientific notation.

SHOW YOUR WORK

11. $\dfrac{3.6 \times 10^4}{120} =$ .... Write your answer in scientific notation.

SHOW YOUR WORK

12. $\dfrac{2.4 \times 10^3}{2.0 \times 10^2}$ = ... Write your answer in scientific notation.

SHOW YOUR WORK

13. $\dfrac{2.7 \times 10^{-3}}{9.0 \times 10^{-2}}$ = ... Write your answer in scientific notation.

SHOW YOUR WORK

14. Eric has 7.4×10^2 quarters in his piggy bank. Each quarter weighs 1.25×10^{-2} pounds. How many pounds do the quarters weigh all together?

SHOW YOUR WORK

15. Sarah is making goodie bags for a big event. She has 120,000 bags and 3.6×10^5 chocolates. How many chocolates can she put in each bag if she wants to distribute the chocolate equally?

SHOW YOUR WORK

We can use what we know about proportional relationships to compare unit rates on a graph.

For example...

The equation $y = 3x$ represents a proportional relationship between x and y.

GRAPH THE LINE REPRESENTED BY THE EQUATION

We can start by plotting (0, 0) because we know that proportional relationships always pass through the origin.

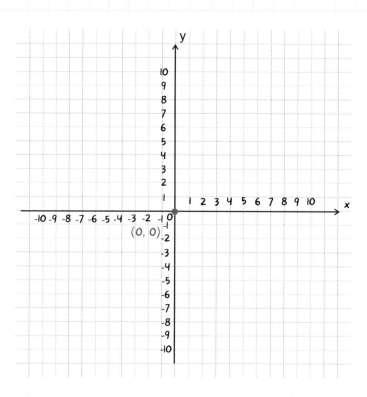

We also know that proportional relationships use the formula $y = mx$, where x and y represent points on the graph. We can use the equation $y = 3x$ to find other points on the line by plugging in values for x.

Equation	Coordinates
$y = 3(1) \rightarrow y = 3$	$(1, 3)$
$y = 3(2) \rightarrow y = 6$	$(2, 6)$
$y = 3(3) \rightarrow y = 9$	$(3, 9)$

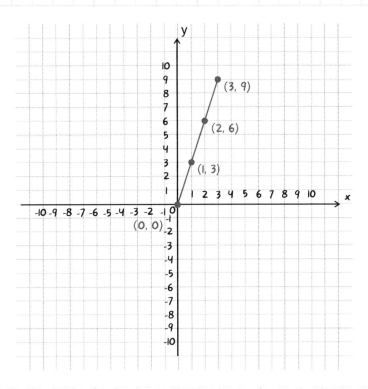

DETERMINE THE UNIT RATE OF CHANGE

Now that we've graphed the line, we can figure out the unit rate of change. The slope of the line represents the unit rate of change.

$$\text{Slope} = \frac{y_2 - y_1}{x_2 - x_1}$$

47

$$\frac{(3-0)}{(1-0)} = \frac{3}{1} = 3$$

COMPARE THIS UNIT RATE OF CHANGE TO ANOTHER UNIT RATE OF CHANGE

We can compare this unit rate of change to other rates of change. For example...

Is the unit rate of change in the graph below greater or less than the unit rate of change in the equation y = 3x?

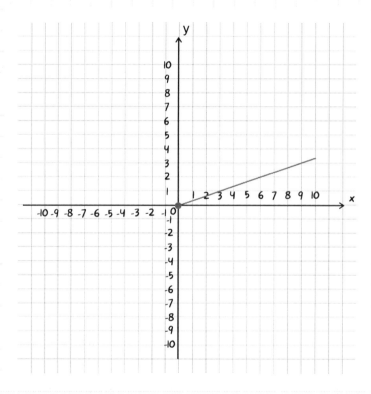

We can tell right away that this unit rate of change is less than the rate of change for line y = 3x because the slope is not as steep.

We can check our answer by calculating the slope of the line and comparing it to the slope of $y = 3x$.

$$\text{Slope} = \frac{(1 - 0)}{(3 - 0)} = \frac{1}{3}$$

The slope of the graph is $\frac{1}{3}$.

Remember that the slope represents the unit rate of change. Therefore the unit rate of change is less.

$$\frac{1}{3} < 3$$

Practice Questions

1. Graph $y = 4.5x$. What is the slope of the line?

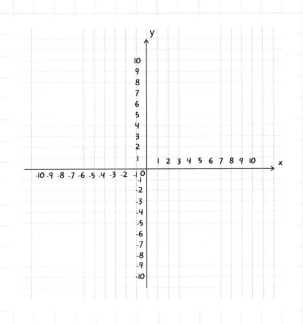

SHOW YOUR WORK

2. Graph $y = \dfrac{1}{2}x$. What is the slope of the line?

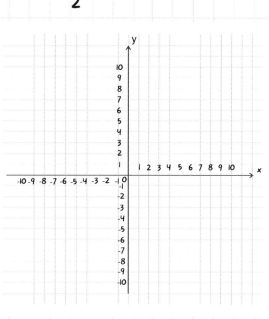

SHOW YOUR WORK

3. Graph $y = \dfrac{3}{4}x$. What is the slope of the line?

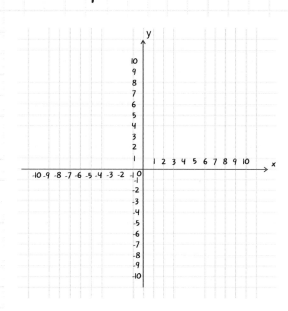

SHOW YOUR WORK

4. Graph y = **6x**. What is the slope of the line?

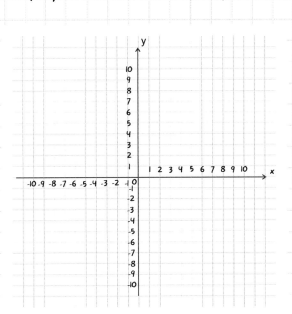

SHOW YOUR WORK

5. Graph y = **3.5x**. What is the slope of the line?

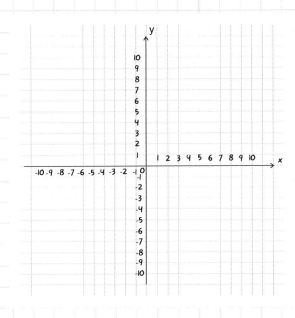

SHOW YOUR WORK

Table A represents a proportional relationship with a constant rate of change. Use the table and coordinate plane to answer questions **6-10**.

Table A

x	1	2	3	4
y	2	4	6	8

Coordinate Plane

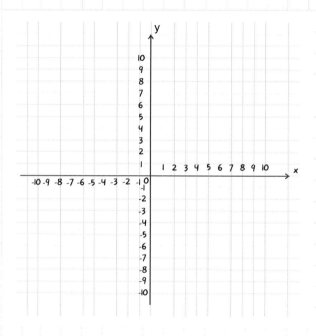

6. What is the unit rate of change for Table A?

SHOW YOUR WORK

7. Graph Table A using the coordinate plane.

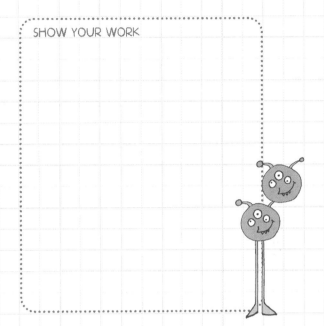

SHOW YOUR WORK

8. Graph the equation y = 4x on the coordinate plane.

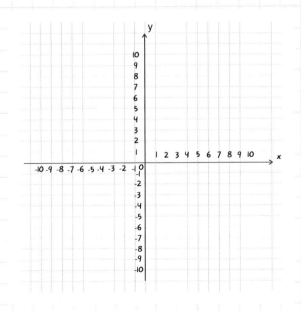

SHOW YOUR WORK

9. What observations can you make by analyzing the two graphs?

A. The line representing Table A is steeper

B. The line representing the equation $y = 4x$ is steeper

C. The lines are parallel

SHOW YOUR WORK

10. Which describes a greater unit rate of change?

A. Table A

B. The equation $y = 4x$

SHOW YOUR WORK

2.2.A | **Graphing Proportional Relationships**

11. Which represents a greater unit rate of change, the graph below or the equation $y = 5x$?

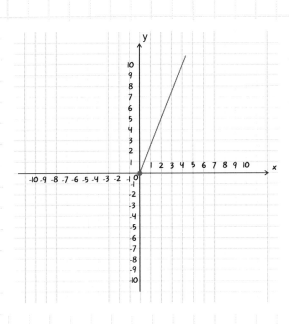

SHOW YOUR WORK

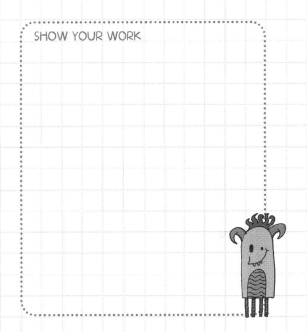

12. Which represents a greater unit rate of change, the table below or the equation $y = \frac{3}{2}x$?

x	0	1	2
y	0	.5	1

SHOW YOUR WORK

55

13. Which represents a greater unit rate of change, the graph below or the equation $y = 3.2x$?

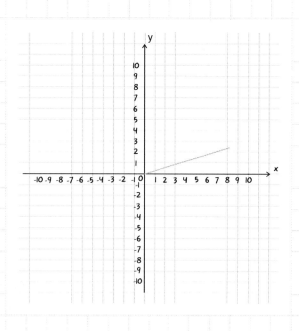

SHOW YOUR WORK

14. Which represents a greater unit rate of change, the table below or the equation $y = \frac{7}{5}x$?

x	0	1	2
y	0	1.2	2.4

SHOW YOUR WORK

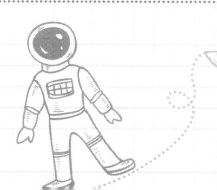
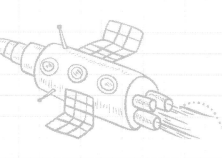

15. Write an equation that represents a unit rate of change less than the unit rate of change in the graph below.

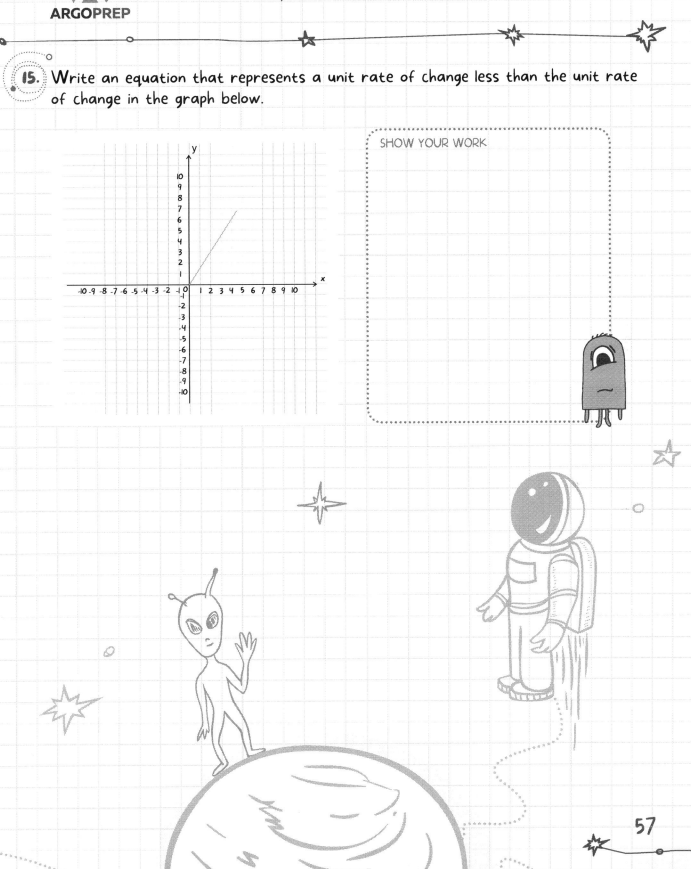

SHOW YOUR WORK

ARGOPREP

Some linear equations do not intersect at the origin. These equations use the slope-intercept formula $y = mx + b$, where m is the slope and b is the y-intercept.

For example...

Graph the linear equation $2y = 4x + 8$.

Step 1: Rewrite the equation

We need to write the equation so that it is in slope-intercept form ($y = mx + b$).

$$2y = 4x + 8$$

$$y = \frac{4x + 8}{2}$$

$$y = 2x + 4$$

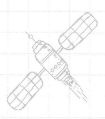

Step 2: Find the y-intercept

Now that the equation is in slope-intercept form, we can see the y-intercept is **(0, 4)**

$$y = 2x + 4$$

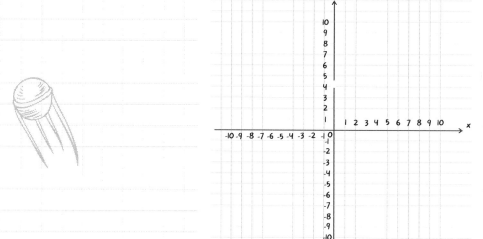

Step 3: Find other points on the line

Now we can use the equation $y = 2x + 4$ to find other points on the line by plugging in values for x.

Equation	Coordinates
$y = 2(1) + 4 \rightarrow y = 6$	(1, 6)
$y = 2(2) + 4 \rightarrow y = 8$	(2, 8)

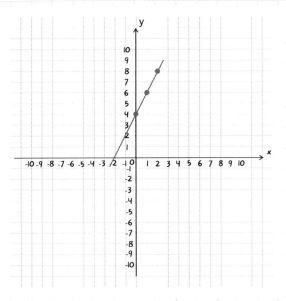

Let's check the slope of the line:

$$\text{Slope} = \frac{(6 - 4)}{(1 - 0)} = \frac{2}{1}$$

$$\text{Slope} = 2$$

IS THE SLOPE CONSTANT?

We can use similar triangles to determine if the slope is constant. If the triangles have the same base and height, then the slope is constant.

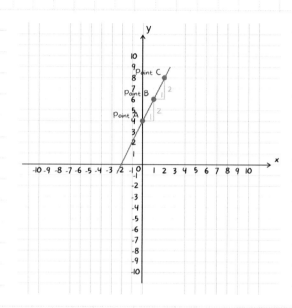

The distance between Point A and Point B is $\frac{2}{1}$, which is equivalent to 2.

The distance between Point B and Point C is also $\frac{2}{1}$, which is equivalent to 2.

ARGOPREP

The slope is constant between the two points.. The slope should remain constant between any two points on the line. Let's try for points A and C.

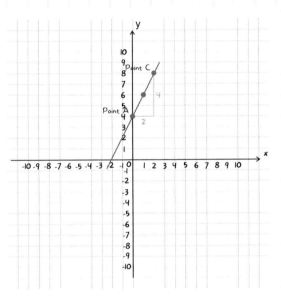

The distance between Point B and Point C is also $\frac{4}{2}$, which is equivalent to 2 ✓

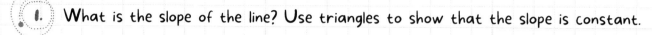

Practice Questions

1. What is the slope of the line? Use triangles to show that the slope is constant.

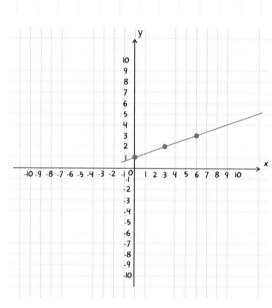

SHOW YOUR WORK

2. What is the slope of the line? Use triangles to show that the slope is constant.

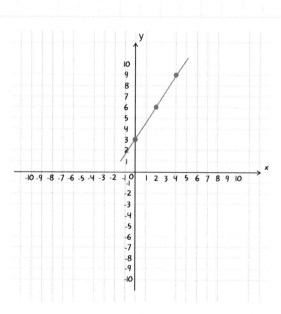

SHOW YOUR WORK

3. What is the slope of the line? Use triangles to show that the slope is constant.

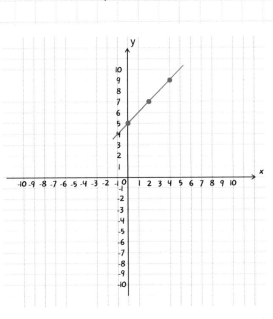

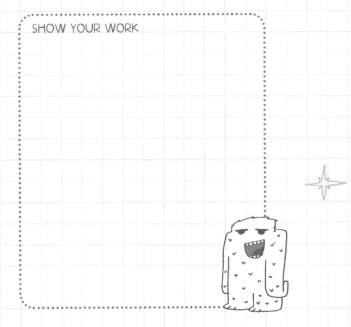

SHOW YOUR WORK

4. What is the slope of the line? Use triangles to show that the slope is constant.

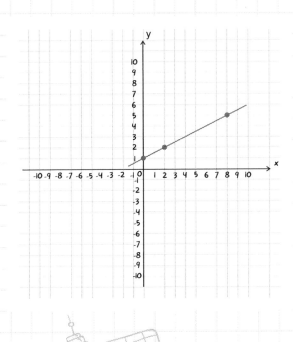

SHOW YOUR WORK

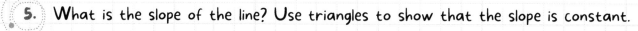

5. What is the slope of the line? Use triangles to show that the slope is constant.

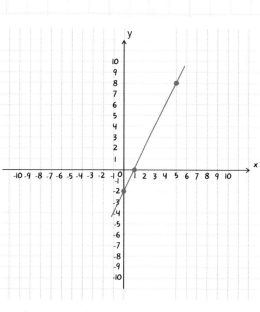

SHOW YOUR WORK

6. What is the slope of the line $5y = 2x$?

SHOW YOUR WORK

7. What is the slope of the line $\frac{1}{2}x = y - 3$?

SHOW YOUR WORK

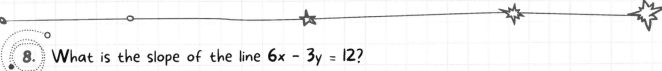

8. What is the slope of the line $6x - 3y = 12$?

SHOW YOUR WORK

9. What is the slope of the line $2y - 2 = 4x$?

SHOW YOUR WORK

10. What is the slope of the line $5x = 3y + 1$?

SHOW YOUR WORK

11. What is the y-intercept for the line $y = 3x + 2$?

SHOW YOUR WORK

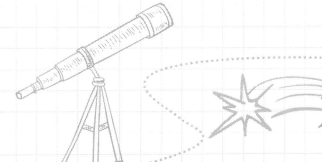

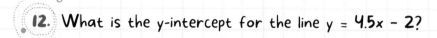

12. What is the y-intercept for the line $y = 4.5x - 2$?

SHOW YOUR WORK

13. What is the y-intercept for the line $4y = 8x - 16$?

SHOW YOUR WORK

14. What is the y-intercept for the line $-2 + y = 5x$?

SHOW YOUR WORK

15. What is the y-intercept for the line $y = 3.5x$?

SHOW YOUR WORK

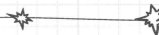

Linear equations can have one solution, many solutions or no solution at all.

LINEAR EQUATIONS WITH ONE SOLUTION

Equations have one solution when **the variables do not cancel out.**

$$12x - 4 = 2x + 1$$

We can solve for x by isolating the variable and simplifying

$$12x - 2x = 1 + 4$$

$$10x = 5$$

$$x = \frac{5}{10}$$

$$x = \frac{1}{2}$$

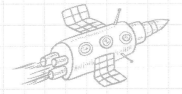

LINEAR EQUATIONS WITH NO SOLUTION

Equations have no solution when **variables cancel each other out and the constants are not equal.**

$$2x + x - 2 = 3x + 5$$

We attempt to solve for x by simplifying the equation and then isolating the variable.

$$3x - 2 = 3x + 5$$

$$3x - 3x - 2 = 5$$

$$-2 = 5$$

-2 is not equal to 5. Therefore, this equation has no solution.

LINEAR EQUATIONS WITH MANY SOLUTIONS

Equations have many solutions when **both sides of the equation are the same.**

$$6x + 2 = 2(3x + 1)$$

We attempt to solve for x by simplifying the equation and then isolating the variable.

$$4x + 2 + 2x = 2(3x + 1)$$

$$6x + 2 = 6x + 2$$

Any number that we substitute for x, will produce the same value. Therefore, x has infinitely many solutions.

Practice Questions

1. The equation $3x + 5 = 7x$ has...

   A. One Solution

   B. No Solution

   C. Many Solutions

   SHOW YOUR WORK

2. The equation $x + 3x - 4 = 2(2x - 2)$ has...

   A. One Solution

   B. No Solution

   C. Many Solutions

   SHOW YOUR WORK

3. The equation $7x - 8 = 5x + 3 + 2x$ has...

A. One Solution

B. No Solution

C. Many Solutions

SHOW YOUR WORK

4. The equation $6(2x - 3) = 4(3x - 2)$ has...

A. One Solution

B. No Solution

C. Many Solutions

SHOW YOUR WORK

5. The equation $x - 0 = 2x + 5$ has...

A. One Solution

B. No Solution

C. Many Solutions

SHOW YOUR WORK

6. The equation $10x - 10 = 2(5x)$ has...

A. One Solution

B. No Solution

C. Many Solutions

SHOW YOUR WORK

7. The equation $8x = 2x(4)$ has...

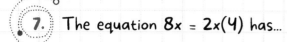

A. One Solution

B. No Solution

C. Many Solutions

SHOW YOUR WORK

8. $4(1 + 2y) = 12y$. Solve for y.

SHOW YOUR WORK

9. $-4 + 3 + 2w = 11 - 4w$. Solve for w.

SHOW YOUR WORK

10. $9(2t - 2) = 4t + 2$. Solve for t.

SHOW YOUR WORK

11. $\frac{1}{2}(6v + 2) = 2v$ Solve for v.

SHOW YOUR WORK

12. $\frac{1}{5}x = 10x$. Solve for x.

SHOW YOUR WORK

13. $8(2w + 3) = 4w$. Solve for w.

SHOW YOUR WORK

14. $-5m + 2m - 1 = 3m + 2$. Solve for m.

SHOW YOUR WORK

15. $s - 10 = 9(s - 2)$. Solve for s.

SHOW YOUR WORK

We can use what we know about linear equations to solve a system of equations. **A system of equations is when more than one linear equation is present in a problem.**

For example...

Kyle and Baylee started their sunflower gardens at the same time. Kyle planted his sunflowers as seeds (0 inches) and they grow 4 inches per week. Baylee planted her sunflowers when they were 2 inches tall and they grow 3 inches each week.

At what week will their sunflowers be the same height?

We can solve this problem using a table, system of equations or a graph.

USING A TABLE

Let **x** represent time in weeks since we are looking at how the plants grow each week.

The first column will represent the height of Kyle's plants, which start at 0 inches and grow 4 inches each week.

The second column represents the height of Baylee's plants, which start at 2 inches and grow 3 inches per week.

x (time in weeks)	y (height of kyle's plants)	y (height of Baylee's plants)
0	0	2
1	4	5
2	8	8
3	12	11

We can see that the plants are the same height a week **2**.

WRITING EQUATIONS

Start by writing an equation for Kyle's sunflowers.

We use the equation $y = mx$ since the y-intercept is **0**. Calculate the slope to determine the value of m.

$$y = mx$$

$$\text{slope} = \frac{y_2 - y_1}{x_2 - x_1} \qquad \text{slope} = \frac{4-0}{1-0}$$

$$y = 4x$$

Now, we need to write an equation for Baylee's sunflowers.

We use the equation $y = mx + b$ since the y-intercept is **2**. Calculate the slope to determine the value of m.

$$y = mx + 2$$

$$\text{slope} = \frac{y_2 - y_1}{x_2 - x_1} \qquad \text{slope} = \frac{5-2}{1-0}$$

$$y = 3x + 2$$

To determine when the equations are equal, we need to solve for x by plugging the first equation in for the *y value* of the second equation.

$$4x = 3x + 2$$
$$4x - 3x = 2$$
$$x = 2$$

Now we need to solve for y. We can solve for y by plugging value of x in both equation. The y value for equation one should be equal to the y value in equation **2**.

$$y = 4(2)$$

$$y = 3(2) + 2$$

$$y = 8 \qquad y = 8$$

$$y = 8$$

At **2** weeks, Kyle and Baylee's sunflowers will be **8** inches tall. ✓

CREATING A GRAPH

Start by graphing the line for Kyle's garden (y = 4x). Then add the line for Baylee's garden to the <u>same</u> graph (y = 3x + 2).

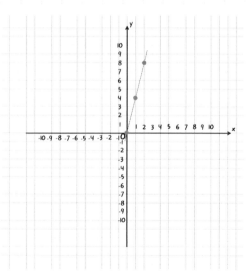
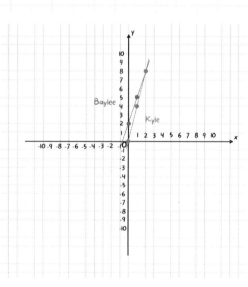

We can see that the lines intersect at **(2,8)**. The intersection represents the point at which the sunflowers will be the same height.

At **2** weeks, Kyle and Baylee's sunflowers will be **8** inches tall. ✓

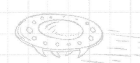

Practice Questions

Use the scenario to answer questions 1 - 6

The grass in Lawn A started at a height of **2** inch and grows 1 inch a month. The grass in Lawn B started at a height of 1 inch and grows **2** inches a month.

1. Complete the tables below.

Time (Months)	1	2	3	4
Lawn A (inches)				
Lawn B (inches)				

2. Write an equation to represent Lawn A's growth per month.

> SHOW YOUR WORK

3. Write an equation to represent Lawn B's growth per month.

> SHOW YOUR WORK

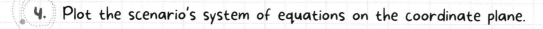

4. Plot the scenario's system of equations on the coordinate plane.

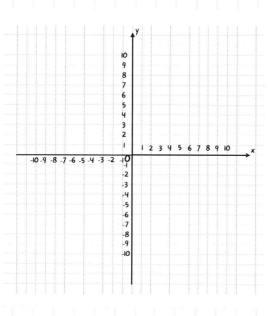

5. At what point do the lines intersect?

SHOW YOUR WORK

6. What does the intersection represent?

SHOW YOUR WORK

7. Graph the system of equations.

$y = x$

$y = \dfrac{1}{2}x + 1$

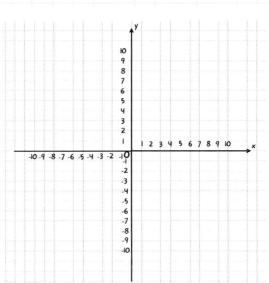

8. Graph the system of equations.

$y = 3x - 3$

$y = \dfrac{3}{2}x$

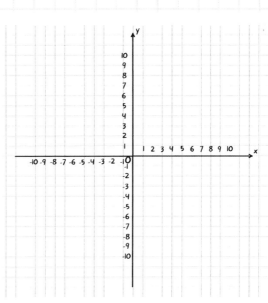

9. Graph the system of equations

$$y = \frac{1}{2}x + 5$$

$$y = 2x$$

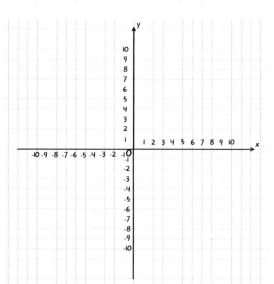

10. Where do the system of equations $y = \frac{2}{3}x - 2$ and $y = \frac{4}{3}x - 4$ intersect? Show your work by solving for x and y.

SHOW YOUR WORK

11. Where do the system of equations $y = \frac{3}{2}x$ and $y = x + 2$ intersect? Show your work by solving for x and y.

SHOW YOUR WORK

12. Where do the system of equations $2y = 3x - 6$ and $y = 2x - 2$ intersect? Show your work by solving for x and y.

SHOW YOUR WORK

13. Where do the system of equations $y = 3.5x - 2$ and $y = 3(x - 2)$ intersect? Show your work by solving for x and y.

SHOW YOUR WORK

Use the scenario below to answer questions 14 - 15.

Dan's hair is **3** inches long and grows **5** inches each year. Sally's hair is **5** inches long and grows **3** inches per year.

14. At what point will Dan's hair be the same length as Sally's hair, if neither person cuts their hair? Draw a table to show your work.

SHOW YOUR WORK

15. Write a system of equations to represent the scenario.

SHOW YOUR WORK

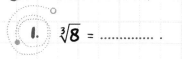

1. $\sqrt[3]{8}$ = ...

> SHOW YOUR WORK

2. $\sqrt{225}$ = ...

> SHOW YOUR WORK

3. $\sqrt{64}$ = ...

> SHOW YOUR WORK

4. $\sqrt[3]{27}$ = ...

> SHOW YOUR WORK

5. $\sqrt[3]{x}$ = 6. Solve for x

> SHOW YOUR WORK

6. $\sqrt[3]{x}$ = 10. Solve for x

> SHOW YOUR WORK

Use the scenario below to answer questions 7 - 9

The baby pool holds **163** gallons of water. The olympic size pool holds **660,253** gallons of water.

7. Which of the following is the best approximation for the volume of the baby pool?

A. 1.6×10^1

B. 1.6×10^2

SHOW YOUR WORK

8. Which of the following is the best approximation for the volume of the olympic size pool?

A. 6.6×10^5

B. 1×10^6

SHOW YOUR WORK

9. The olympic size pool is approximately .... times as large as the baby pool.

SHOW YOUR WORK

10. $3 \times 10^4 + 3,500 = $ .... Write your answer in scientific notation.

SHOW YOUR WORK

11. $2.4 \times 10^{-3} + .04 = $ .... Write your answer in scientific notation.

SHOW YOUR WORK

12. $325 - 2.5 \times 10^2$ = ... Write your answer in scientific notation.

SHOW YOUR WORK

13. $8,150 - 1.5 \times 10^2$ = ... Write your answer in scientific notation.

SHOW YOUR WORK

Use the equation below to answer questions 14 – 16

The equation $y = 2(4x)$ represents a proportional relationship between x and y.

14. Graph the equation using the coordinate plane.

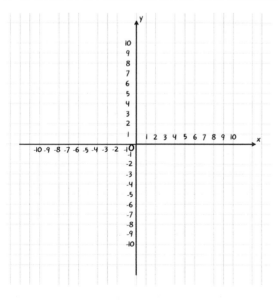

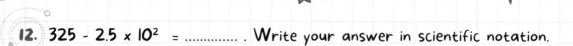

15. What is the unit rate of change?

SHOW YOUR WORK

16. Is the unit rate of change in the graph below greater or less than the unit rate of change in the equation?

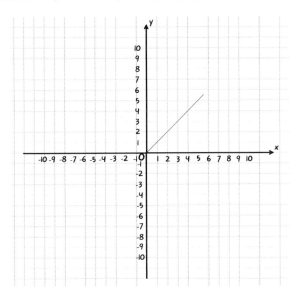

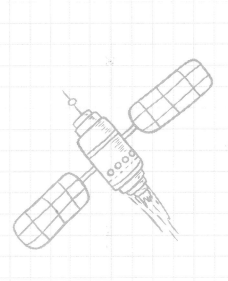

17. The equation $15x + 5 = 5(3x + 2)$ has...

A. One Solution

SHOW YOUR WORK

B. No Solution

C. Many Solutions

18. The equation $2x + x - 12 = 3(x - 4)$ has...

A. One Solution

B. No Solution

C. Many Solutions

SHOW YOUR WORK

Use the scenario below to answer questions 19-20.

Lauren's tomato plant is 1 inch long and grows **3** inches each week. Hannah's tomato plant is **3** inches long and grows **2** inch per week.

19. At what point will Lauren and Hannah's plants be the same height? Show your work.

SHOW YOUR WORK

20. Write a system of equations to represent the growth of the tomato plants.

SHOW YOUR WORK

NOTES

Chapter 3:
Functions

3.1.A. Intro to Functions page 88

3.1.B. Comparing Functions. page 97

3.1.C. Nonlinear Functions page 106

3.2.A. Constructing Functions page 113

3.2.B. Analyzing Functional Relationships page 121

3.3. Chapter Test page 130

ARGOPREP
STUDY SMARTER, NOT HARDER

A function is a rule that assigns exactly one output for each input. In other words, each x-value has only one y-value.

The following representations are functions since each input (x-value) only has one output (y-value).

x	y
0	1
1	2
2	3

$$y = \frac{5}{2}x + 1$$

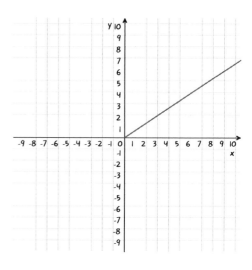

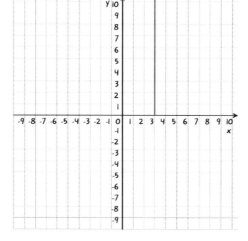

The following representations are not functions because some inputs (x-values) have more than one output (y-values).

x	y
-1	1
-1	-1
0	0

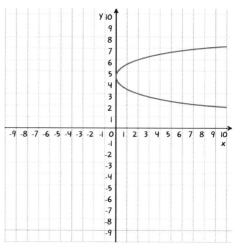

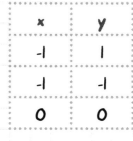

Practice Questions

1. Is the representation below a function? Explain your answer.

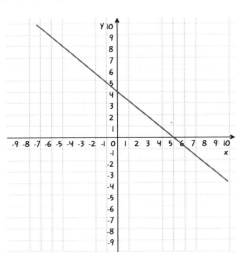

SHOW YOUR WORK

2. Is the representation below a function? Explain your answer.

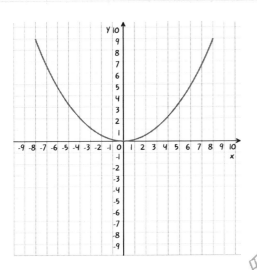

SHOW YOUR WORK

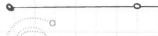
3. Is the representation below a function? Explain your answer.

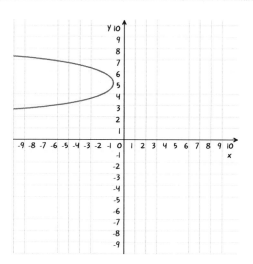

SHOW YOUR WORK

4. Is the representation below a function? Explain your answer.

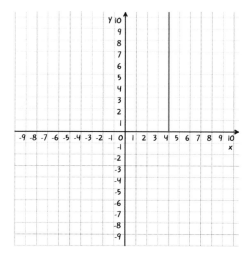

SHOW YOUR WORK

5. Is the representation below a function? Explain your answer.

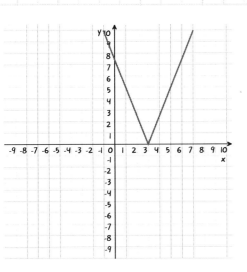

SHOW YOUR WORK

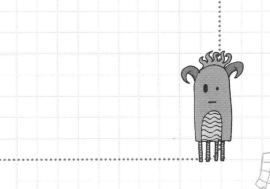

6. Is the representation below a function? Explain your answer.

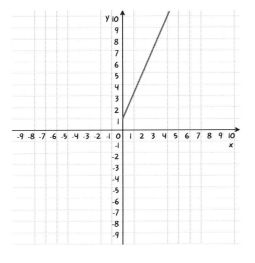

SHOW YOUR WORK

3.1.A | Intro to Functions

7. Is the representation below a function? Explain your answer.

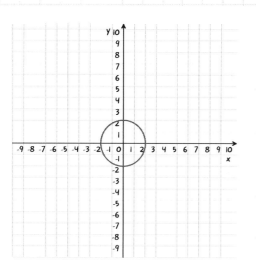

SHOW YOUR WORK

8. Is the representation below a function? Explain your answer.

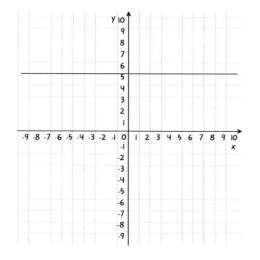

SHOW YOUR WORK

9. Is the representation below a function? Explain your answer.

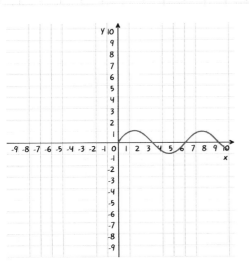

SHOW YOUR WORK

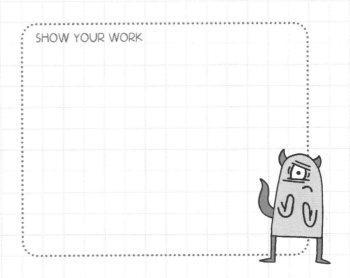

10. Is the representation below a function? Explain your answer.

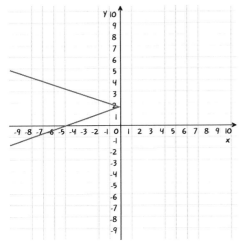

SHOW YOUR WORK

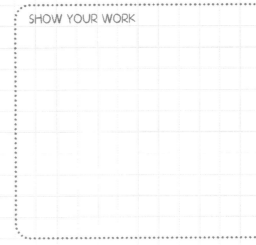

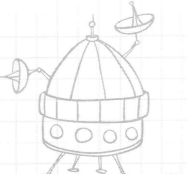

11. Which set of ordered pairs does not represent a function?

A. (5, 2), (3, 1), (6, 2), (4,1)   B. (3, -2), (1, 2), (3, 0), (5, 4)

SHOW YOUR WORK

12. Which set of ordered pairs does not represent a function?

A. (-1, -2), (0, 0), (1, -2)   B. (1, 2), (0, 0), (1, -2)

SHOW YOUR WORK

13. Which set of ordered pairs does not represent a function?

A. (0, 0), (1, 3), (0, 6)   B. (0, 0), (1, 3), (2, 0)

SHOW YOUR WORK

14. Which set of ordered pairs does not represent a function?

A. (7, -7), (1, -1), (-7, 7)   B. (3, 2), (4, 4), (3, 0)

SHOW YOUR WORK

15. Which set of ordered pairs does not represent a function?

A. (0, 0), (2, 2), (4, 0), (2, -2)   **B.** (0, 0), (2, 2) (4, 0), (6, 2)

SHOW YOUR WORK

16. Is (color, votes) represented as a function? Explain your answer.

Color	Student Votes
Pink	3
Blue	8
Orange	5

SHOW YOUR WORK

17. Is (hair style, meal ordered) represented as a function? Explain your answer.

Hair Type	Meal Ordered
Pony Tail	Mac & Cheese
Mohawk	Cheese Burger
Pig Tails	Hot Dog
Bald	Mac & Cheese

SHOW YOUR WORK

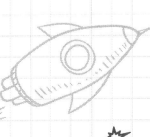

18. Can the miles run be represented as a function of student age? Explain your answer.

Student Age	Miles Ran
10	5
11	6
12	8
10	2
11	6
9	3

SHOW YOUR WORK

19. Can the number of hot dogs eaten be represented as a function of eye color? Explain your answer.

Eye Color	Blue	Green	Brown	Hazel	Blue	Hazel
Hot Dog	3	2	5	1	2	4

SHOW YOUR WORK

20. Can the amount of rain be represented as a function of the city? Explain your answer.

Rainfall	2"	4"	7"	5"	2"
City	Raleigh	Chicago	Seattle	Orlando	Los Angeles

SHOW YOUR WORK

We can use what we know about functions to compare two different representations. For example...

Compare the representations. Which one has a greater **y-intercept**?

Function 1

$$y = 4x + 2$$

Function 2

x	y
0	3
1	5
2	7

we know that the equation is written in slope-intercept form, $y = mx + b$, where b represents the y-intercept.

y-intercept = 2

we know that the y-intercept is where the line crosses the y-axis, which is when $x = 0$.

y-intercept = 3

Function **2** has a greater y-intercept ✓

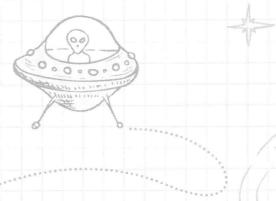

Compare the representations. Which one has a greater **rate of change**?

Function 1	Function 2

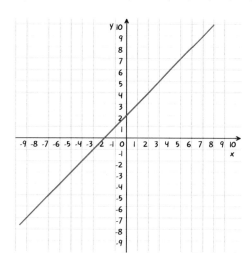

$$y = \frac{1}{2}x - 3$$

we know that the unit rate of change is equal to the slope of the line.

we know that the equation is written in slope-intercept form, $y = mx + b$, where m represents the unit rate of change

unit rate of change = 1

unit rate of change = $\frac{1}{2}$

Function 1 has a greater unit rate of change ✓

Practice Questions

Use the representations below to answer questions 1-6

Representation A

Representation B

$$y = 2x + 3$$

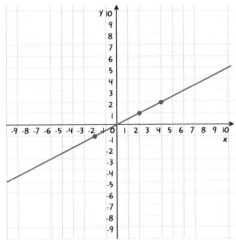

1. What is the slope of Representation A?

> SHOW YOUR WORK

2. What is the slope of Representation B?

> SHOW YOUR WORK

3. Which representation has a greater unit rate of change?

SHOW YOUR WORK

4. What is the y-intercept for Representation A?

SHOW YOUR WORK

5. What is the y-intercept for Representation B?

SHOW YOUR WORK

6. Which representation above has a greater y-intercept?

SHOW YOUR WORK

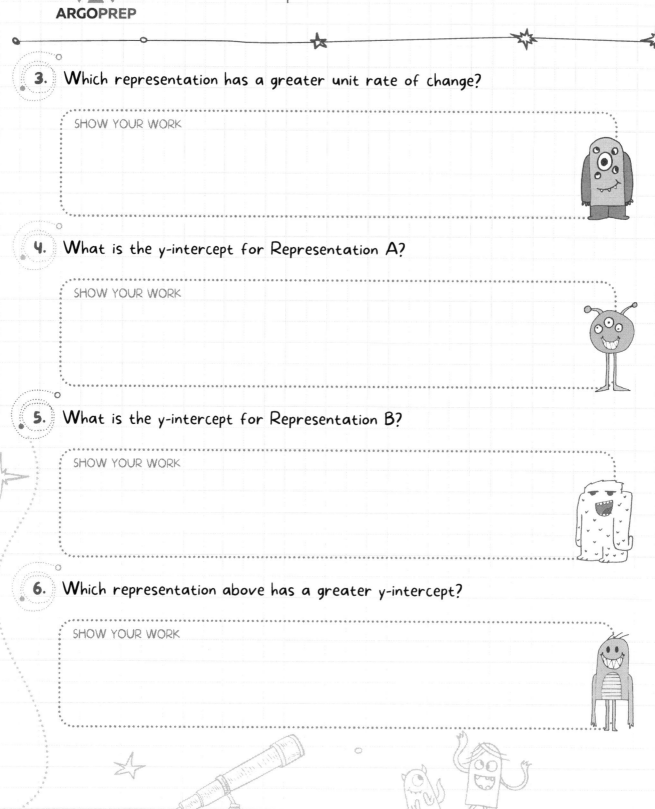

Use the representations below to answer questions 7-12

Representation A

x	y
-3	1
-2	4
-1	7

Representation B

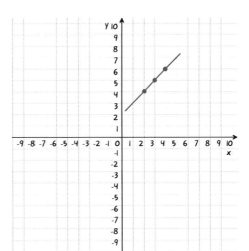

7. What is the slope of Representation A?

SHOW YOUR WORK

8. What is the slope of Representation B?

SHOW YOUR WORK

101

9. Which representation above has a greater unit rate of change?

SHOW YOUR WORK

10. What is the y-intercept for Representation A?

SHOW YOUR WORK

11. What is the y-intercept for Representation B?

SHOW YOUR WORK

12. Which representation above has a greater y-intercept?

SHOW YOUR WORK

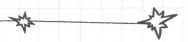

Use the representations below to answer questions 13-15

Representation A

$$2y = 4x + 5$$

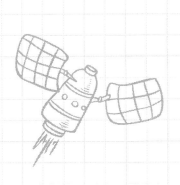

Representation B

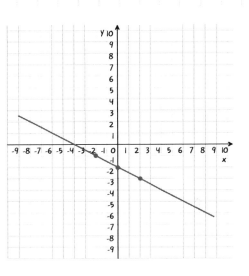

13. Rewrite Representation A in slope-intercept form.

SHOW YOUR WORK

14. What is the slope of Representation B?

SHOW YOUR WORK

15. Which representation has a greater unit rate of change?

SHOW YOUR WORK

16. Which representation above has a greater y-intercept?

Representation A shows the number of girls scout cookies (y) that Heather sold on each day of the sale (x). Representation B shows the number of girls scout cookies (y) that Jinger sold on each day of the sale (x). Use the representations below to answer questions 16-20

Heather

x	y
1	3
5	6
9	9

Jinger

$3y = 9x - 3$

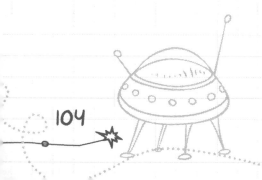

17. Rewrite Jinger's equation in slope-intercept form.

SHOW YOUR WORK

18. Who sold cookies at a faster rate?

SHOW YOUR WORK

19. Who sold more cookies on day 1?

SHOW YOUR WORK

20. Who sold more cookies on day 5?

SHOW YOUR WORK

Functions assign exactly one output for each input, but they do not have to be linear. For example, the three representations below are functions...

Nonlinear Functions

$f(x) = |4|$

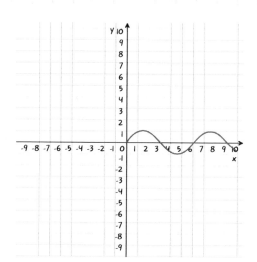

x	y
-1	3
0	0
1	3

It's important to be able to distinguish a linear function from a nonlinear function. The easiest way to do this is to look at the slope of a function. If it is constant, the function is linear. If it is not constant, the function is nonlinear.

Practice Questions

1. Which of the following represents a linear function? Explain your reasoning.

A. $y = \dfrac{1}{2}x$

B. $y = x^2$

SHOW YOUR WORK

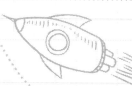

2. Which of the following represents a linear function? Explain your reasoning.

A. $y = 4.5x + 2$

B. $y = |x|$

SHOW YOUR WORK

3. Which of the following represents a linear function? Explain your reasoning.

A. $y = 4x - 2$

B. $y = 2x^3 + 3$

SHOW YOUR WORK

4. Which of the following represents a linear function? Explain your reasoning.

A.

x	y
-3	1
0	0
3	4

B.

x	y
-1	4
0	6
1	8

SHOW YOUR WORK

5. Which of the following represents a linear function? Explain your reasoning.

A.

x	y
1	1
2	0
3	-1
4	-2

B.

x	y
-2	4
-1	0
0	0
1	4

SHOW YOUR WORK

6. Which of the following represents a linear function? Explain your reasoning.

A.

x	y
-1	10
0	0
-1	2

B.

x	y
5	10
4	7
3	4

SHOW YOUR WORK

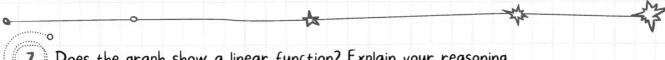

7. Does the graph show a linear function? Explain your reasoning.

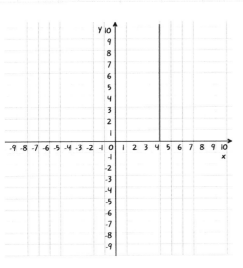

SHOW YOUR WORK

8. Does the graph show a linear function? Explain your reasoning.

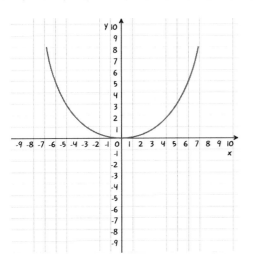

SHOW YOUR WORK

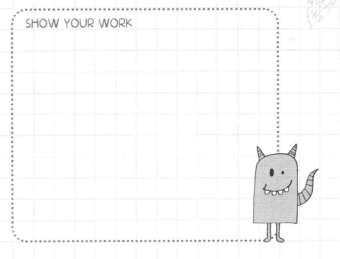

9. Does the graph show a linear function? Explain your reasoning.

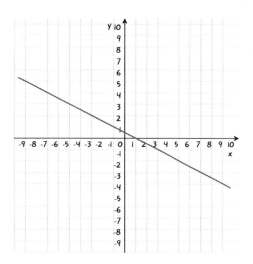

SHOW YOUR WORK

10. Does the graph show a linear function? Explain your reasoning.

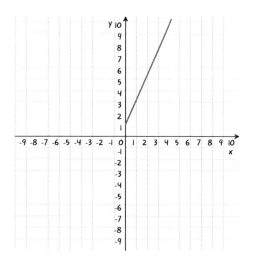

SHOW YOUR WORK

11. (-3, 0) and (0, 3) are points on the graph of a linear function. Which point also lies on the graph of this function?

A. (1, 1) **B.** (9, 12)

SHOW YOUR WORK

12. (5, 7) and (3, 5) are points on the graph of a linear function. Which point also lies on the graph of this function?

A. (4, 6) **B.** (1, 3)

SHOW YOUR WORK

13. (-6, -2) and (3, 10) are points on the graph of a linear function. List two other points that could lie on the graph of this function,

SHOW YOUR WORK

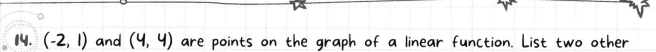

14. (-2, 1) and (4, 4) are points on the graph of a linear function. List two other points that could lie on the graph of this function,

> SHOW YOUR WORK

15. (5, 5) and (-5, 3) are points on the graph of a linear function. List two other points that could lie on the graph of this function,

> SHOW YOUR WORK

NOTES

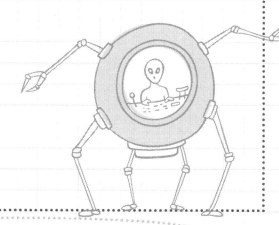

We can use what we know about functions to write our own linear equations.

For example...

Write an equation that models the relationship shown in the table.

x	8	12
y	2	4

We know that we need to write the equation in slope-intercept form **y = mx + b**

$y \rightarrow$ dependent variable

$x \rightarrow$ independent variable

$m \rightarrow$ slope

$b \rightarrow$ y-intercept

<u>Step 1:</u> Determine Slope

$$\text{Slope} = \frac{y_2 - y_1}{x_2 - x_1}$$

$$m = \frac{4 - 2}{12 - 8} = \frac{2}{4}$$

$$m = \frac{1}{2}$$

$$y = \frac{1}{2}x + b$$

Step 2: Determine Y-Intercept

Plug in x_1 and y_1 to isolate b.

$$(2) = \frac{1}{2}(8) + b$$

$$2 = 4 + b$$

$$-2 = b$$

$$y = \frac{1}{2}x - 2 \checkmark$$

Practice Questions

1. Write an equation that models the linear relationship in the table.

x	2	4
y	1	5

SHOW YOUR WORK

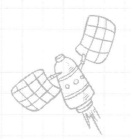

2. Write an equation that models the linear relationship in the table.

x	3	6
y	4	5

SHOW YOUR WORK

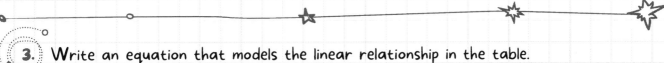

3. Write an equation that models the linear relationship in the table.

x	-6	6
y	7	5

SHOW YOUR WORK

4. Write an equation that models the linear relationship in the table.

x	8	5
y	2	-1

SHOW YOUR WORK

5. Write an equation that models the linear relationship in the table.

x	3	15
y	6	10

SHOW YOUR WORK

6. Write an equation that models the linear relationship in the graph.

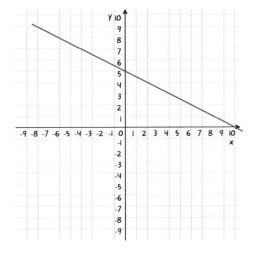

SHOW YOUR WORK

7. Write an equation that models the linear relationship in the graph.

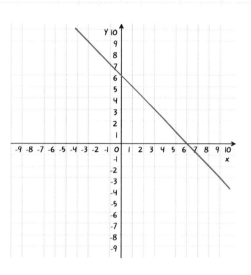

SHOW YOUR WORK

8. Write an equation that models the linear relationship in the graph.

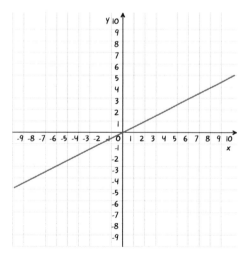

SHOW YOUR WORK

9. Write an equation that models the linear relationship in the graph.

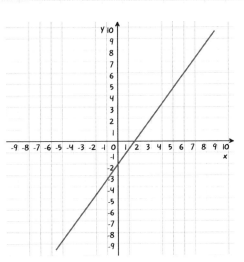

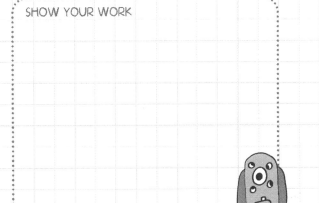

SHOW YOUR WORK

10. Write an equation that models the linear relationship in the graph.

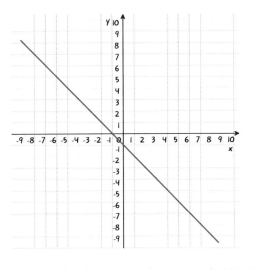

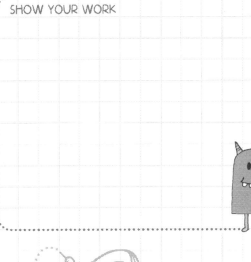

SHOW YOUR WORK

11. Write an equation for the line that has a rate of change of **5** and passes through the point **(1,5)**.

SHOW YOUR WORK

12. Write an equation for the line that has a rate of change of $\frac{2}{3}$ and passes through the point **(3, 5)**.

SHOW YOUR WORK

13. Write an equation for the line that has a rate of change of **3** and passes through the point **(-1, 2)**.

SHOW YOUR WORK

14. Write an equation for the line that has a rate of change of $\frac{1}{3}$ and passes through the point **(3, 4)**.

SHOW YOUR WORK

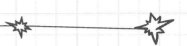

15. Write an equation for the line that has a rate of change of **2** and passes through the point (**-2, 0**).

SHOW YOUR WORK

16. The coaches purchase **2** uniforms for every student in addition to the **10** uniforms they already have from last year. Write a function for the number of uniforms (u) and the number of students (s).

SHOW YOUR WORK

17. Sarah is saving up to buy a new bike. Her parents gave her **$10** to start. After that, she earns **$10** each time she does a chore for one of her neighbors. Write a function for the number of dollars (d) and the number of chores (c).

SHOW YOUR WORK

18. Lara is selling girl scout cookies. Her grandma buys **5** boxes before the sale begins. After that, Lara sells **3** boxes each day. Write a function for the number of boxes (b) and the number of days (d).

SHOW YOUR WORK

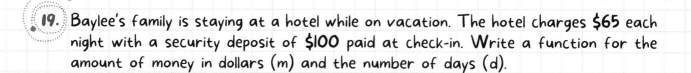

19. Baylee's family is staying at a hotel while on vacation. The hotel charges **$65** each night with a security deposit of **$100** paid at check-in. Write a function for the amount of money in dollars (m) and the number of days (d).

SHOW YOUR WORK

20. Brandon rents scuba gear at the beach. He charges **$25** per hour plus a **$50** security deposit. Write a function for the amount of money in dollars (m) and the number of hours (h).

SHOW YOUR WORK

NOTES

We can use what we know about functions to analyze functional relationships on a graph.

For example...

The graph below shows the number of miles each person swam, y, during each week of training, x.

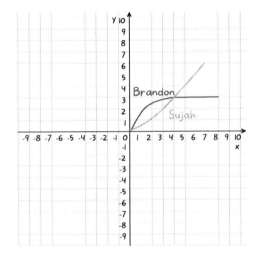

During what week did Brandon and Sujah swim the same number of miles?

We can answer this question by finding where the two lines intersect because this is when the lines have the same x-values as well as the same y-values.

Brandon and Sujah both swim three miles during Week 4.

Who swims more miles during Week 5?

We can determine who swam more at any given point by looking at the y-values.

We can see that when x = 5, Brandon's y-value is 3 and Sujah's y-value is 5.

Sujah swims two more miles than Brandon during week 5.

Practice Questions

Use the graph to answer questions 1-5.

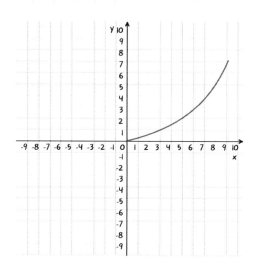

1. As x increases, y ....

   A. Decreases

   B. Increases

   C. Stays the Same

   SHOW YOUR WORK

2. The rate of change for y as a function of x is ....

   A. Constant   **B.** Not Constant

   SHOW YOUR WORK

3. The function is ....

A. Linear   **B.** Nonlinear

SHOW YOUR WORK

4. The value of y when x equals **8** is ....

SHOW YOUR WORK

5. The value of y when x equals **5** is .... times larger than when x equals **3**.

SHOW YOUR WORK

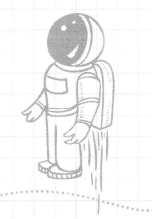

The graph below shows the number of miles each person swam, y, during each week of training, x. Use the graph to answer questions 6-10.

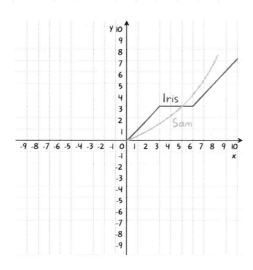

6. During the first 3 weeks ....

   A. Iris swam more miles

   B. Sam swam more miles

   C. They swam the same amount

   SHOW YOUR WORK

7. During which week did Iris and Sam swim the same number of miles?

   A. Week 2

   B. Week 5

   C. Week 9

   SHOW YOUR WORK

8. Which person continues to increase the number of miles swam per week?

A. Iris

B. Sam

C. Both

D. Neither

SHOW YOUR WORK

9. Sam swims .... more mile(s) than Iris during Week **6**.

SHOW YOUR WORK

10. Iris's mileage .... from Week **3** to Week **6**.

A. Decreases

B. Increases

C. Stays the same

SHOW YOUR WORK

The graph below shows the number of dollars earned, y, during each hour of the bake sale, x. Use the graph to answer questions 11-15.

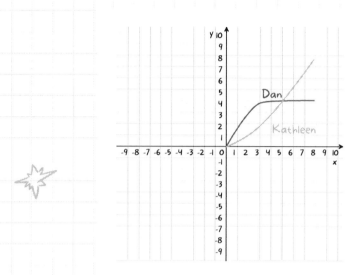

11. Who makes more money at the beginning of the bake sale?

A. Dan

B. Kathleen

C. They make the same amount

SHOW YOUR WORK

12. Who makes the most money by the end of the bake sale?

A. Dan

B. Kathleen

C. They make the same amount

SHOW YOUR WORK

13. At what hour have Kathleen and Dan made the same amount of money?

A. Hour 2

B. Hour 5

C. Hour 7

SHOW YOUR WORK

14. Dan makes .... money as Kathleen at Hour 2.

A. half as much

B. twice as much

C. three times as much

SHOW YOUR WORK

15. Which graph shows a linear function?

A. Dan's graph

B. Kathleen's graph

C. Both graph

D. Neither graph

SHOW YOUR WORK

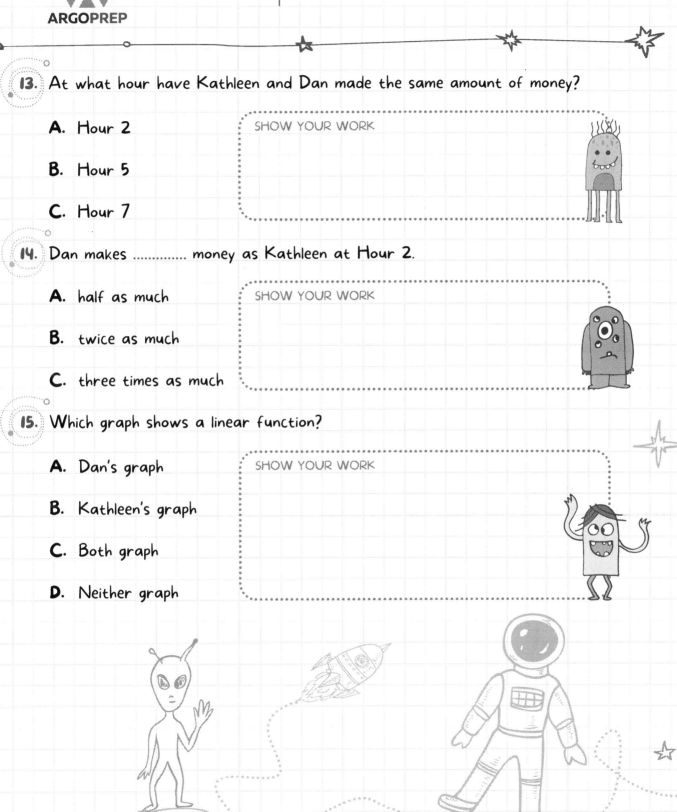

Use the coordinate plane to answer questions 16-20.

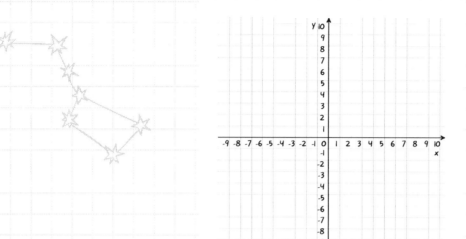

16. Sarah is training for a walkathon. She walks two miles on day 1. She continues to increase the number of miles she walks by **2** miles each day for the next **5** days. Graph a line representing the total miles walked, y, in **5** days.

17. Lars is also training for a walkathon. He walks one mile on day 1. He continues to increase the number of miles he walks by **1** miles each day for the next **5** days. Graph a line representing the total miles walked, y, in **5** days.

18. Which person's graph represents a linear function?

A. Sarah

B. Lars

C. Both

D. Neither

SHOW YOUR WORK

19. Sarah walks .... miles as Lars on day **5**.

A. half as many

B. twice as many

C. three times as many

SHOW YOUR WORK

20. Who walks more miles in **5** days?

A. Sarah

B. Lars

C. They walk the same amount

SHOW YOUR WORK

1. Is the representation below a function? Explain your answer.

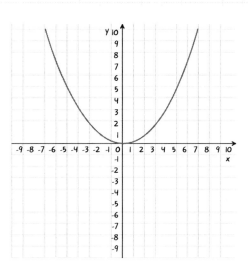

SHOW YOUR WORK

2. Is the representation below a function? Explain your answer.

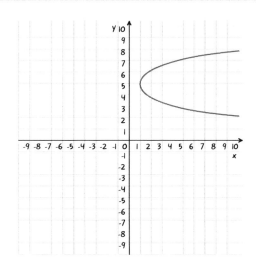

SHOW YOUR WORK

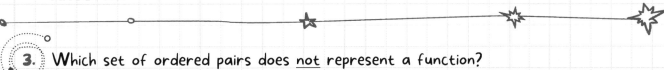

3. Which set of ordered pairs does <u>not</u> represent a function?

A. (0, -4), (5, -2), (2, -3), (5,-6)　　　**B.** (-3, -6), (0, -5), (3, -4), (6, -3)

SHOW YOUR WORK

4. Which set of ordered pairs does <u>not</u> represent a function?

A. (-1, 0), (-3, 1), (3, 1)　　　**B.** (-1, 0), (-3, 1), (-1, -1)

SHOW YOUR WORK

5. Which of the following represents a linear function? Explain your reasoning.

x	y
1	1
2	2
3	3
4	4

A.

x	y
-2	1
-1	0
0	-1
1	1

B.

SHOW YOUR WORK

6. Which of the following represents a linear function? Explain your reasoning.

A.

x	y
6	-3
10	0
12	-1

B.

x	y
5	1
4	-1
3	-3

SHOW YOUR WORK

7. (0, 5) and (2, 10) are points on the graph of a linear function. Which point also lies on the graph of this function?

A. (-2, 0)   B. (1, 0)

SHOW YOUR WORK

8. (12, 9) and (6, 8) are points on the graph of a linear function. Which point also lies on the graph of this function?

A. (0, 7)   B. (0, 6)

SHOW YOUR WORK

Use the representations below to answer questions 9-10

Representation A

x	y
0	2
4	6
16	18

Representation B

$$5y = 15x + 5$$

9. Which representation has a greater rate of change?

> SHOW YOUR WORK

10. Which representation has a greater y-intercept?

> SHOW YOUR WORK

11. Write an equation that models the linear relationship in the table.

x	2	6
y	8	10

SHOW YOUR WORK

12. Write an equation that models the linear relationship in the table.

x	1	4
y	4	1

SHOW YOUR WORK

13. Write an equation that models the linear relationship in the graph.

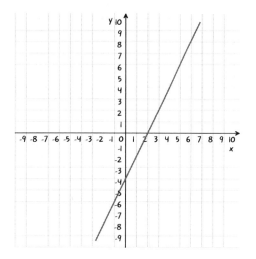

SHOW YOUR WORK

14. Write an equation that models the linear relationship in the graph.

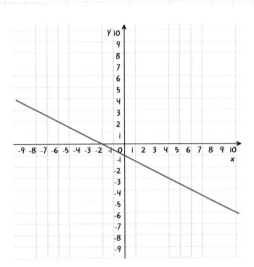

SHOW YOUR WORK

15. Write an equation for the line that has a rate of change of $\frac{1}{3}$ and passes through the point (3, 2)

SHOW YOUR WORK

16. Write an equation for the line that has a rate of change of **-2** and passes through the point (5, 7)

SHOW YOUR WORK

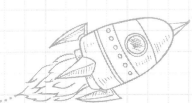

The graph below shows the ounces of water drank, y, from a **5** oz water bottle during each mile of a race, x. Use the graph to answer questions 17-20.

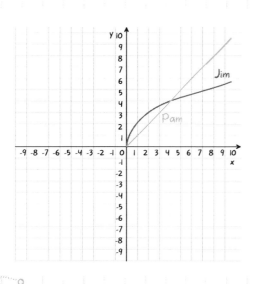

SHOW YOUR WORK

17. .... drank more during the first part of the race.

A. Pam

B. Jim

C. They drank the same amount

SHOW YOUR WORK

18. At what mile did Pam and Jim have the same amount of water remaining?

A. Mile 3

B. Mile 4

C. Mile 5

SHOW YOUR WORK

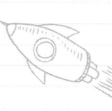

19. Jim had drank .... ounce(s) more than Pam by Mile **2**.

A. 1

B. 2

C. 3

SHOW YOUR WORK

20. Who finished their **5** ounces of water first?

A. Pam

B. Jim

C. They finished their water at the same time

SHOW YOUR WORK

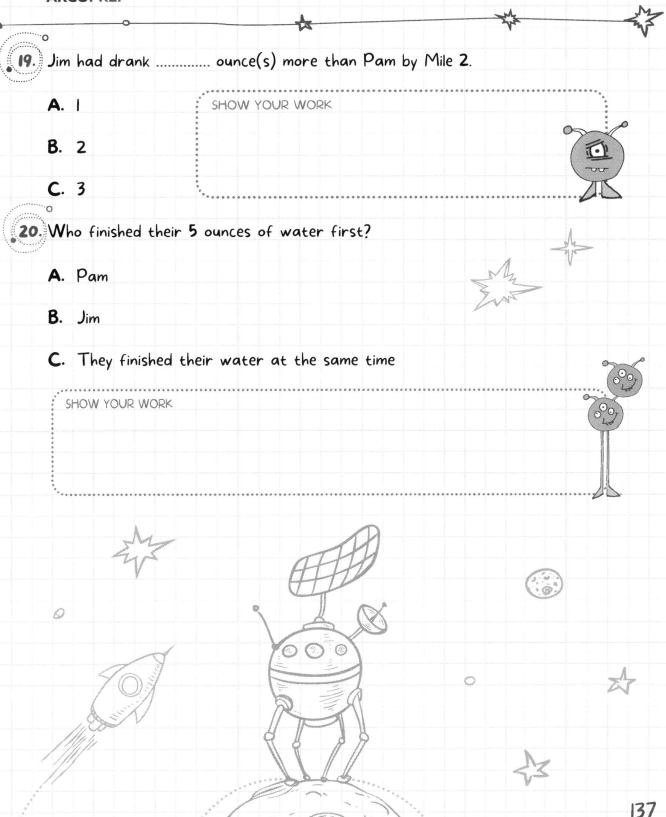

Chapter 4:
Geometry

4.1.A. Experimenting with Rotations, Reflections and Translations page 140

4.1.B. Congruent Figures page 150

4.1.C. Transformations on a Coordinate Plane page 158

4.1.D. Similar Figures page 168

4.2.A. Intro to Pythagorean Theorem page 176

4.2.B. Applying the Pythagorean Theorem - Part I page 181

4.2.C. Applying the Pythagorean Theorem - Part II page 185

4.3. Volume of Cones, Cylinders and Spheres page 192

4.4. Chapter Test page 197

ARGOPREP
STUDY SMARTER, NOT HARDER

A rotation moves a point around the origin in a circular shape. Each quadrant represents **90** degrees.

For example...

The rotation of A is shown as A'

The arrow represents the degree of rotation (90°)

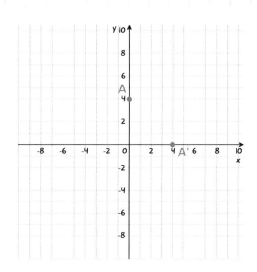

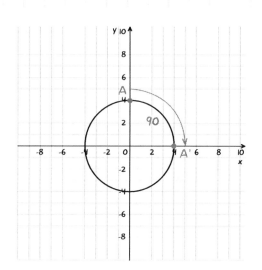

A reflection moves a point perpendicularly across a line so that it looks like the images reflection.

For example...

The reflection of ABC is shown as A'B'C'   The arrow represents the line of reflection

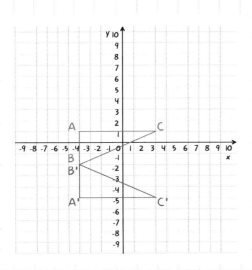

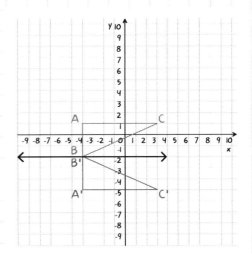

A translation moves a point a specific number of units up or down and left or right.

For example...

The translation of ABC is shown as A'B'C'   The dotted line shows the movement
(4 down, 2 right)

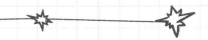

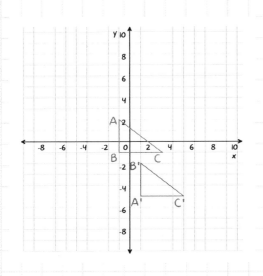

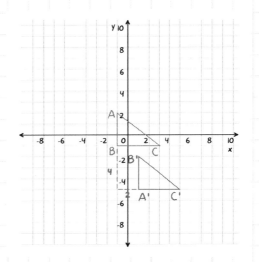

141

Practice Questions

1. Point A' is the image of Point A under a rotation around the origin. Determine the angle of rotation.

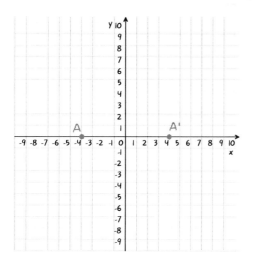

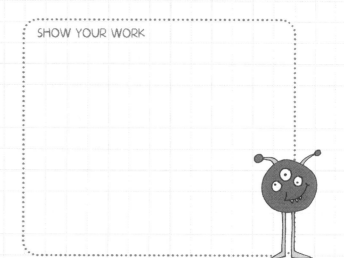

SHOW YOUR WORK

2. Point B' is the image of Point B under a rotation around the origin. Determine the angle of rotation.

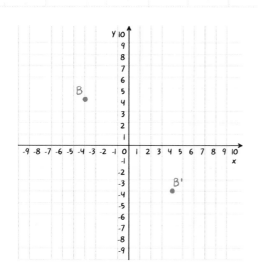

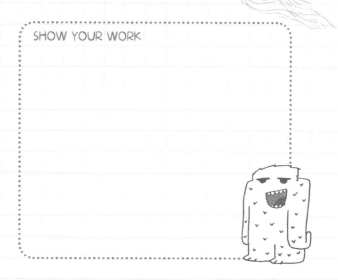

SHOW YOUR WORK

3. Point C' is the image of Point C under a rotation around the origin. Determine the angle of rotation.

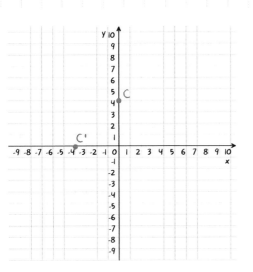

SHOW YOUR WORK

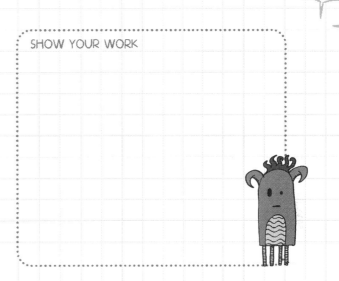

4. Point D' is the image of Point D under a rotation around the origin. Determine the angle of rotation.

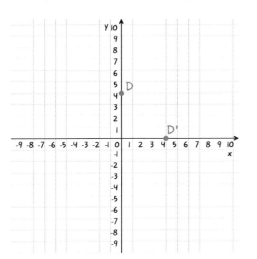

SHOW YOUR WORK

5. Point E' is the image of Point E under a rotation around the origin. Determine the angle of rotation.

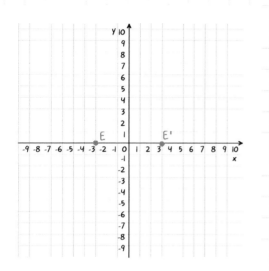

SHOW YOUR WORK

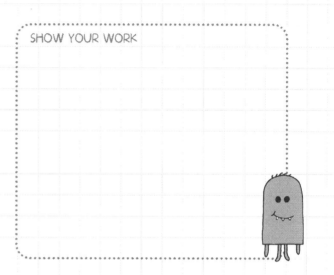

6. Draw the line of reflection for △ABC onto △A'B'C'

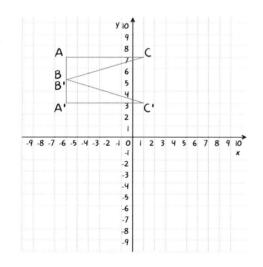

SHOW YOUR WORK

7. Draw the line of reflection for △ABC onto △A'B'C'

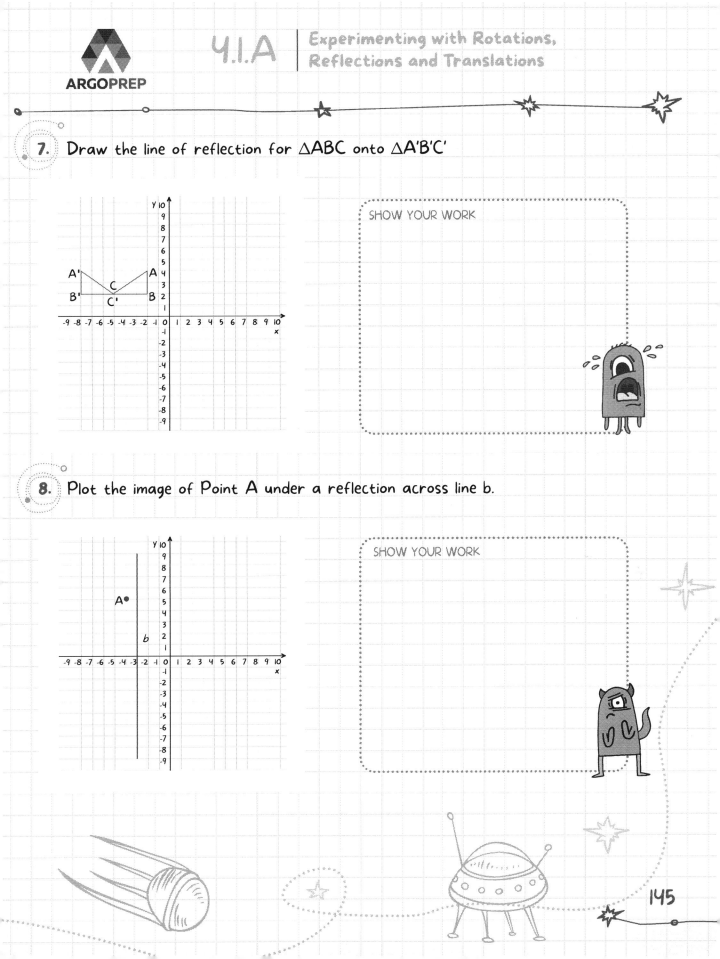

SHOW YOUR WORK

8. Plot the image of Point A under a reflection across line b.

SHOW YOUR WORK

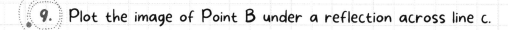

9. Plot the image of Point B under a reflection across line c.

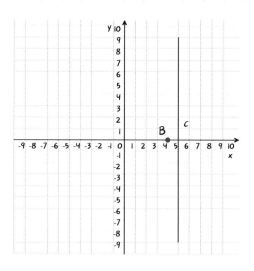

SHOW YOUR WORK

10. Plot the image of Point B under a reflection across line m.

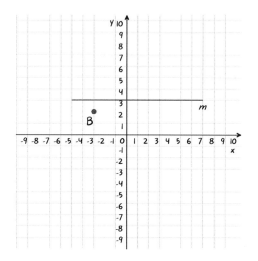

SHOW YOUR WORK

11. Plot the image of Point A under a translation of **3** units to the left and **5** units up.

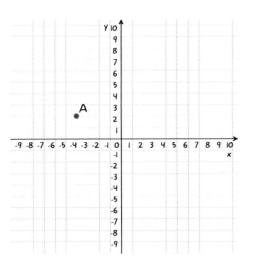

SHOW YOUR WORK

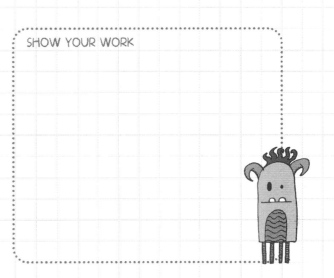

12. Plot the image of Point A under a translation of **2** units to the right and **3** units up.

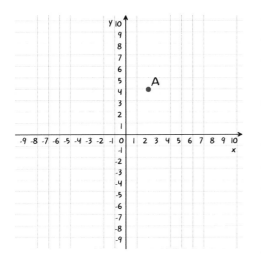

SHOW YOUR WORK

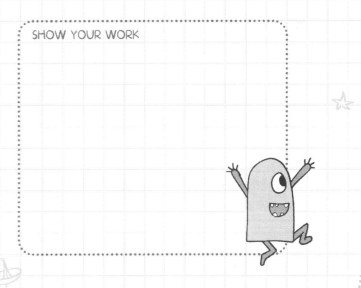

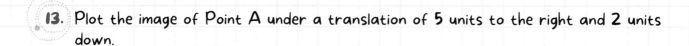

13. Plot the image of Point A under a translation of **5** units to the right and **2** units down.

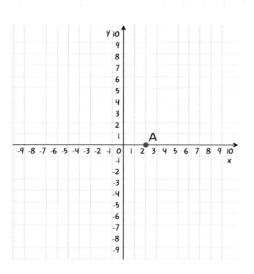

SHOW YOUR WORK

14. Plot the image of Point A under a translation of **1** unit to the left and **4** units up.

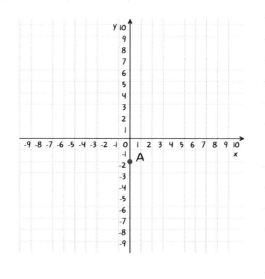

SHOW YOUR WORK

15. Plot the image of Point A under a translation of **3** units to the left and **1** units down.

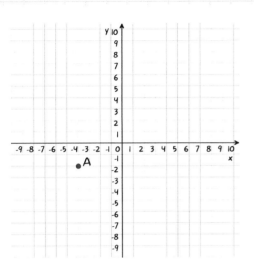

SHOW YOUR WORK

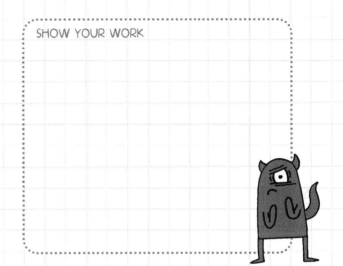

NOTES

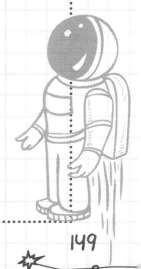

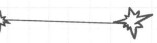

Congruent figures (≅) have the same shape and size. You can create congruent shapes using a sequence of rotations, reflections and translations.

For example...

Rectangle ABCD is rotated **90°** clockwise around the origin to form rectangle EFGH.

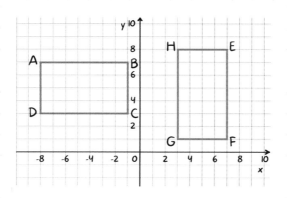

Which statement is true about the relationship between rectangle ABCD and rectangle EFGH?

    A. $\overline{AB} \cong \overline{HG}$

    B. $\overline{DA} \cong \overline{HE}$

    C. $\overline{CD} \cong \overline{FG}$

    D. $\overline{BC} \cong \overline{GF}$

In order to determine which sides align, we need to rotate rectangle ABCD **90°** clockwise.

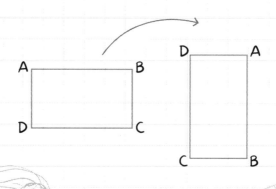

Once the rectangle is rotated, we can compare it to the congruent shape. Notice that the order of the sides matters. For example, DA ≅ HE but BC is <u>not</u> congruent to GF.

The answer is B.
DA ≅ HE

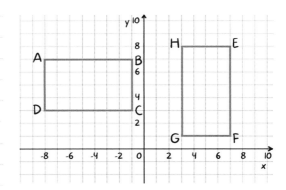

Practice Questions

1. What single transformation was applied to ABCD to get WXYZ?

   A. Reflection

   B. Rotation

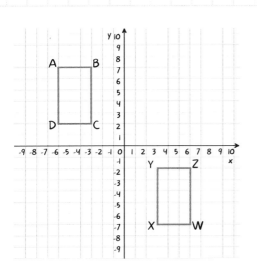

SHOW YOUR WORK

2. What single transformation was applied to ABCD to get WXYZ?

A. Translation

B. Reflection

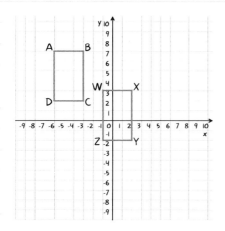

SHOW YOUR WORK

3. What single transformation was applied to Triangle A to get Triangle B?

A. Reflection

B. Translation

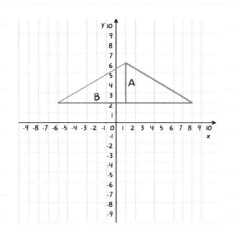

SHOW YOUR WORK

4. What single transformation was applied to Triangle A to get Triangle B?

A. Translation

B. Reflection

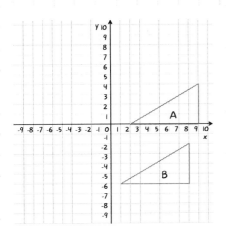

SHOW YOUR WORK

5. What single transformation was applied to Triangle A to get Triangle X?

A. Rotation

B. Reflection

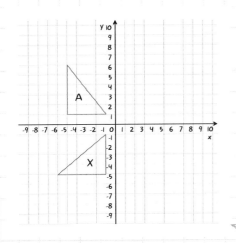

SHOW YOUR WORK

Rectangle ABCD is rotated 180° clockwise around the origin to form rectangle WXYZ. Use the rectangles to answer questions 6 - 8.

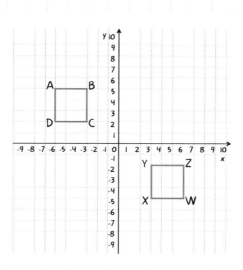

6. Which of the following statements is true?

A. ABCD ≅ YZWX

B. ABCD ≅ ZWXY

C. ABCD ≅ WXYZ

D. ABCD ≅ XYZW

SHOW YOUR WORK

7. Which side of WXYZ is congruent to AB?

A. YZ

B. ZW

C. WX

D. XY

SHOW YOUR WORK

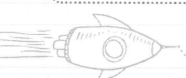

8. Which side of WXYZ is congruent to DC?

A. ZY

B. WX

C. YZ

D. XW

SHOW YOUR WORK

9. △A'B'C' represents a translation of △ABC by .... units to the right and .... units down.

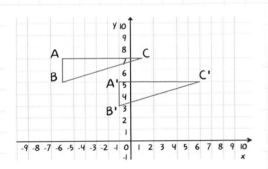

SHOW YOUR WORK

10. Point A' (-1, 2) represents Point A (7, 8) under a translation. Point A' represents a translation by .... units to the left and .... units down

SHOW YOUR WORK

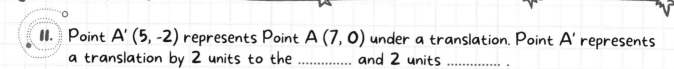

11. Point A' (5, -2) represents Point A (7, 0) under a translation. Point A' represents a translation by **2** units to the .... and **2** units ....

> SHOW YOUR WORK

12. Point A' (4, 3) represents Point A (2, 1) under a translation. Point A' represents a translation by .... units to the .... and **2** units up.

> SHOW YOUR WORK

Triangle XYZ represents a reflection of triangle ABC across the y-axis. Use the triangles to answer questions 13 - 15.

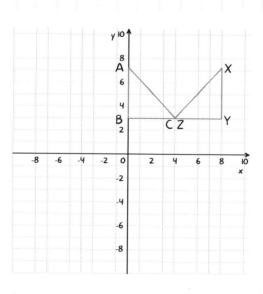

13. $\overline{BC} \cong$ ....

    A. $\overline{YZ}$

    B. $\overline{XY}$

    C. $\overline{ZY}$

    D. $\overline{XZ}$

SHOW YOUR WORK

14. $\overline{AC} \cong$ ....

    A. $\overline{XZ}$

    B. $\overline{ZY}$

    C. $\overline{YZ}$

    D. $\overline{YX}$

SHOW YOUR WORK

15. How would the image change if Triangle ABC were reflected over the x-axis?

SHOW YOUR WORK

We can use coordinate planes to understand how transformations affect different shapes. For example, *dilations* are a type of transformation that changes the size of an object.

SIZING UP

Plot the image of point A under dilation about the origin with a scale of **2**.

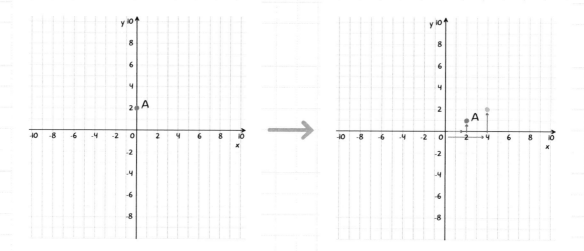

The blue dot represents the dilation because it is twice the distance from the origin as the original point.

SIZING DOWN

Plot the image of point A under dilation about the origin with a scale of $\frac{1}{2}$.

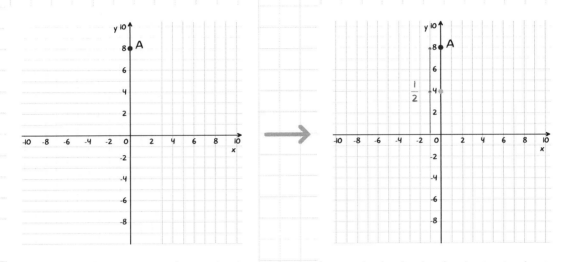

The blue dot represents the dilation because it is half the distance from the origin as the original point.

4.1.C | Transformations on a Coordinate Plane

Practice Questions

1. Plot the image of point A under dilation about the origin with a scale of **2**.

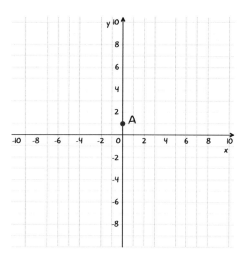

SHOW YOUR WORK

2. Plot the image of point A under dilation about the origin with a scale of **3**.

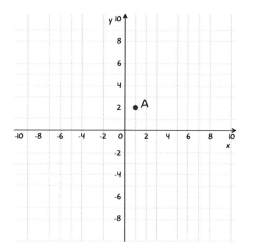

SHOW YOUR WORK

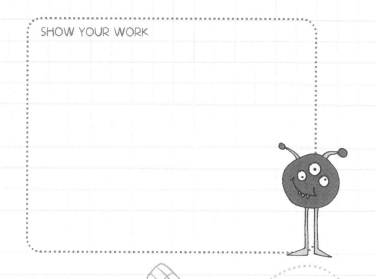

3. Plot the image of point A under dilation about the origin with a scale of $\frac{1}{4}$.

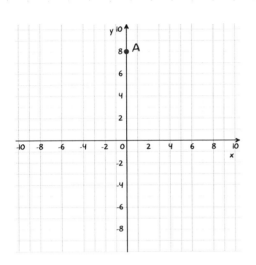

SHOW YOUR WORK

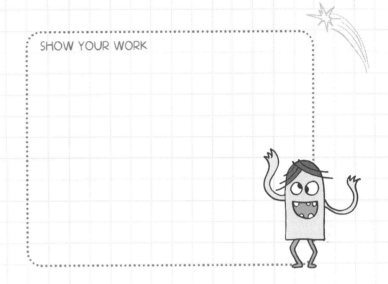

4. Plot the image of point A under dilation about the origin with a scale of $\frac{1}{2}$.

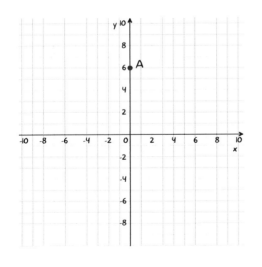

SHOW YOUR WORK

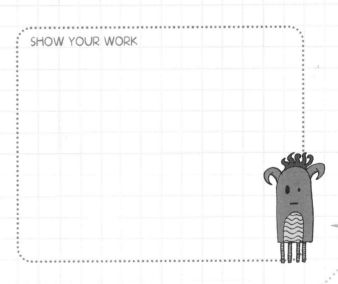

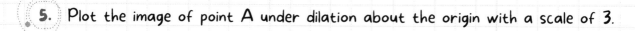

5. Plot the image of point **A** under dilation about the origin with a scale of **3**.

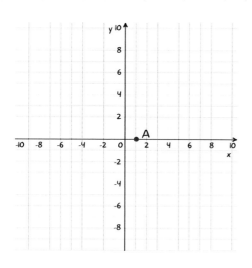

SHOW YOUR WORK

6. Plot the image of Triangle **A** under dilation about the origin with a scale of **2**.

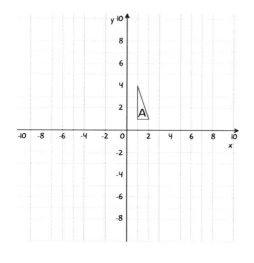

SHOW YOUR WORK

7. Plot the image of Triangle A under dilation about the origin with a scale of $\frac{1}{2}$.

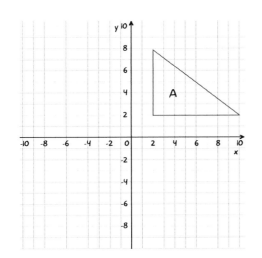

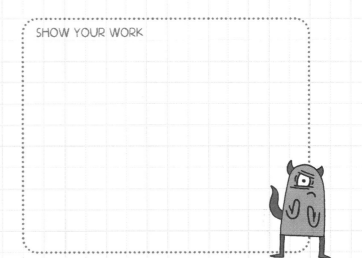

SHOW YOUR WORK

Use the coordinate plane below to answer questions 8 - 11.

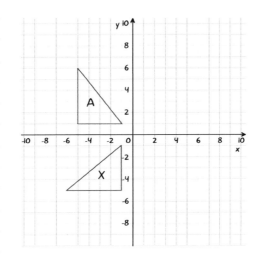

163

8. Triangle X is the image of Triangle A rotated .... degrees about the origin.

A. 90

B. 180

C. 270

D. 360

SHOW YOUR WORK

9. $(-1, -5) \cong (-5, 1)$

A. True   B. False

SHOW YOUR WORK

10. $(-1, -1) \cong (-1, 1)$

A. True   B. False

SHOW YOUR WORK

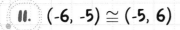

11. $(-6, -5) \cong (-5, 6)$

A. True

B. False

SHOW YOUR WORK

Use the coordinate plane below to answer questions 12 - 13.

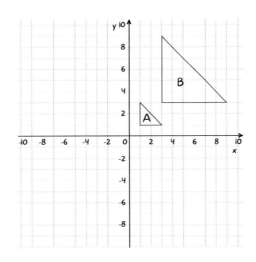

12. Triangle B is the image of Triangle A under dilation about the origin with a scale of ....

SHOW YOUR WORK

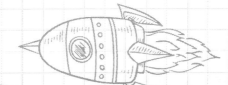

13. Triangle A is the image of Triangle B under dilation about the origin with a scale of ....

SHOW YOUR WORK

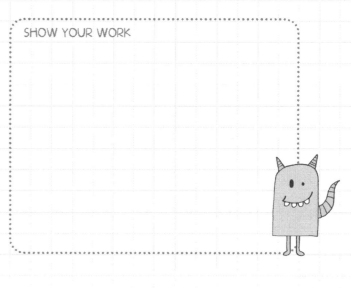

14. Describe the translation of Triangle A using coordinates.

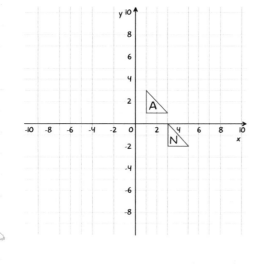

SHOW YOUR WORK

15. Describe the translation of Triangle A using coordinates.

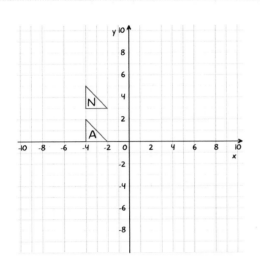

SHOW YOUR WORK

NOTES

Similar figures (~) have congruent angles and proportional corresponding side lengths. In other words, they are the exact same shape, but may not be the same size or orientation. To check if two objects are similar, you can map one onto the other using a series of transformations.

For example...

Are the triangles below similar?

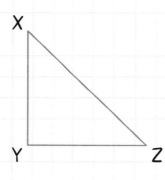

Start by looking for a series of transformations that enable you to map the smaller triangle onto the larger triangle. For this example, we can start by rotating EFG 270°

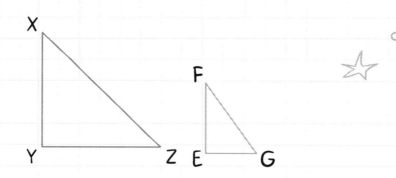

Next, we can translate Point E onto Point Y.

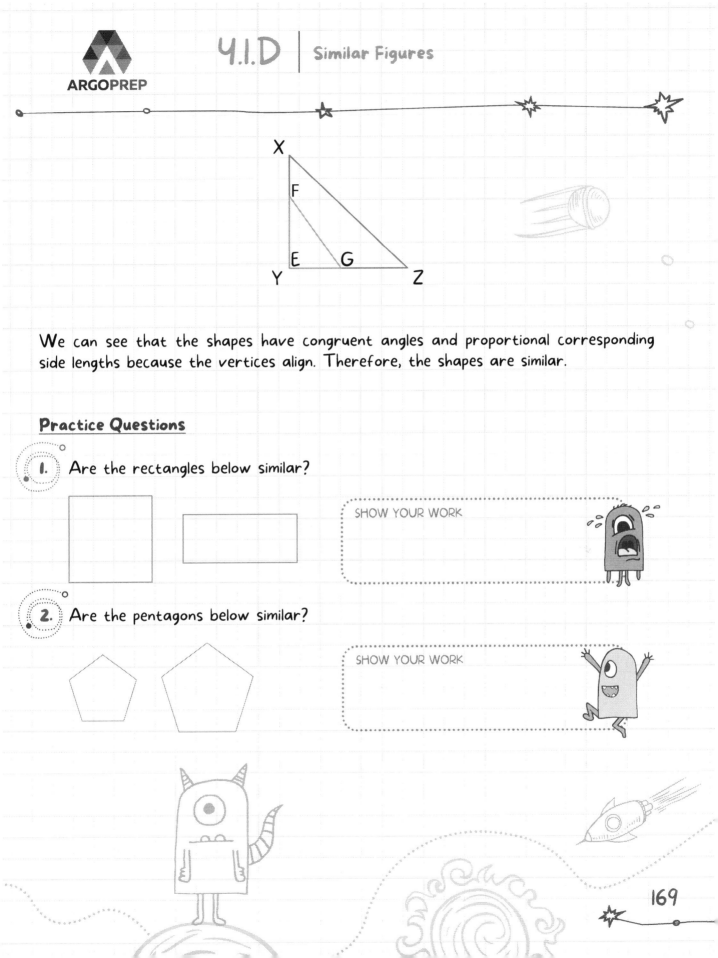

We can see that the shapes have congruent angles and proportional corresponding side lengths because the vertices align. Therefore, the shapes are similar.

Practice Questions

1. Are the rectangles below similar?

SHOW YOUR WORK

2. Are the pentagons below similar?

SHOW YOUR WORK

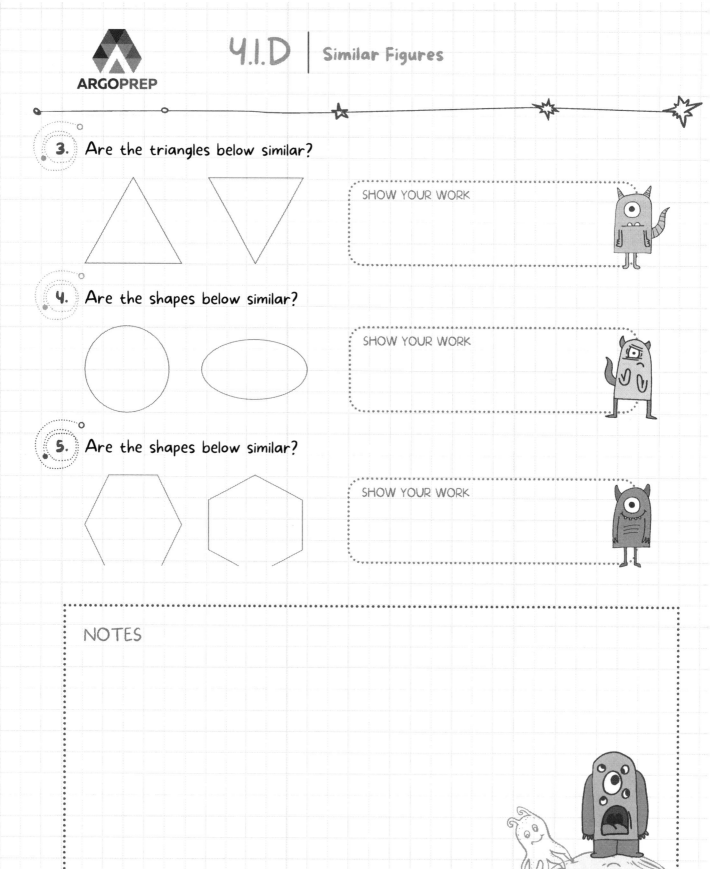

3. Are the triangles below similar?

SHOW YOUR WORK

4. Are the shapes below similar?

SHOW YOUR WORK

5. Are the shapes below similar?

SHOW YOUR WORK

NOTES

Use the coordinate plane below to answer questions 6 - 7.

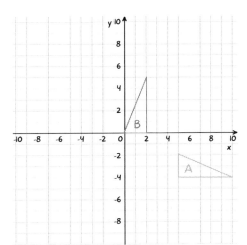

6. Use the coordinate plane to determine if the triangles are similar.

SHOW YOUR WORK

7. Explain why the figures are/aren't similar.

SHOW YOUR WORK

Use the coordinate plane below to answer questions 8 - 9.

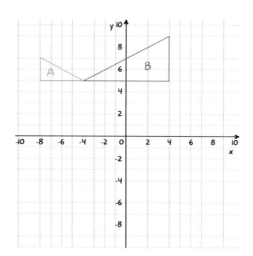

8. Use the coordinate plane to determine if the triangles are similar.

SHOW YOUR WORK

9. Explain why the figures are/aren't similar.

SHOW YOUR WORK

Use the coordinate plane below to answer questions 10 - 11.

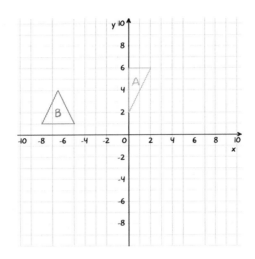

10. Use the coordinate plane to determine if the triangles are similar.

SHOW YOUR WORK

11. Explain why the figures are/aren't similar.

SHOW YOUR WORK

Use the coordinate plane below to answer questions 12 - 15.

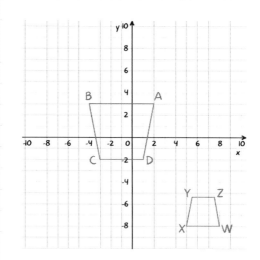

12. Use the coordinate plane to determine if the figures are similar.

SHOW YOUR WORK

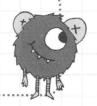

13. Explain why the figures are/aren't similar.

SHOW YOUR WORK

14. Draw a set of similar figures using the coordinate plane below.

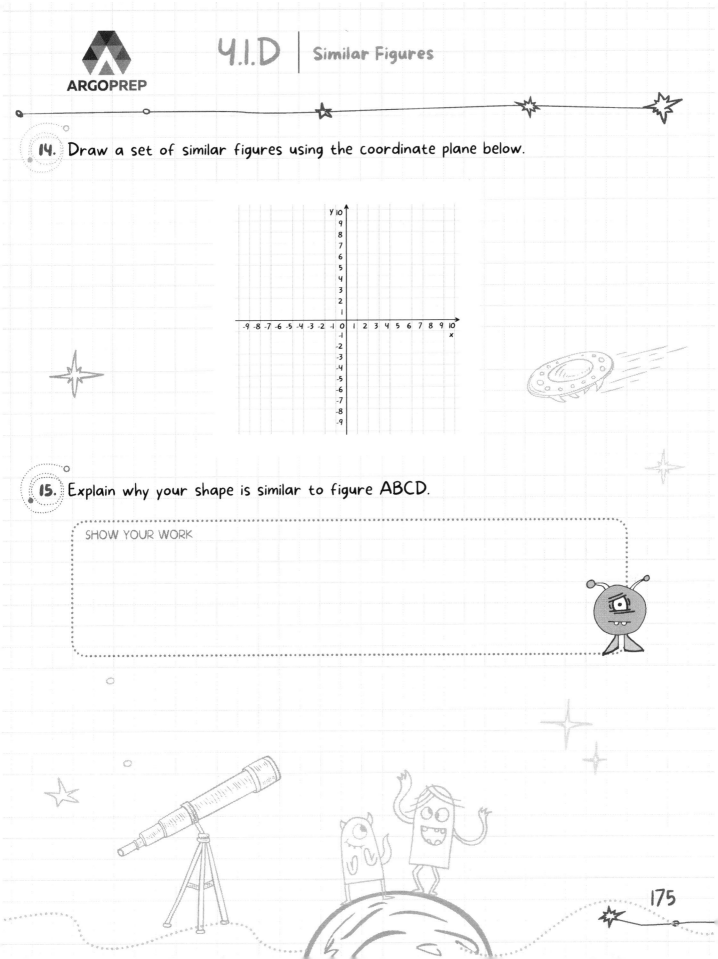

15. Explain why your shape is similar to figure ABCD.

SHOW YOUR WORK

The *pythagorean theorem* states that the square of a right triangle's hypotenuse is equal to the sum of the squares of the other two sides.

$$a^2 + b^2 = c^2$$

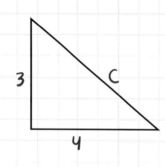

$$3^2 + 4^2 = c^2$$

$$9 + 16 = 25$$

$$\sqrt{25} = 5$$

$$C = 5$$

We can visualize the theorem by drawing squares...

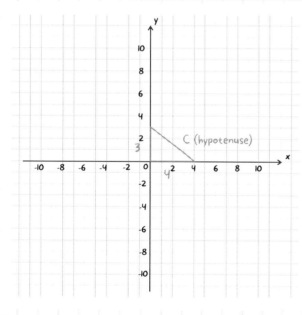

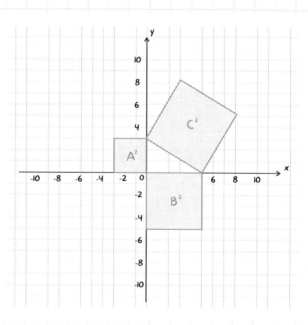

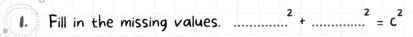

Practice Questions

1. Fill in the missing values. ....^{2} + ...^{2} = c^2

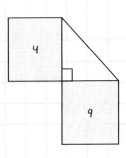

SHOW YOUR WORK

2. Fill in the missing values. ....^{2} + ...^{2} = c^2

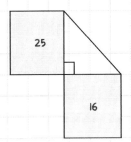

SHOW YOUR WORK

3. Fill in the missing values. ....^{2} + ...^{2} = c^2

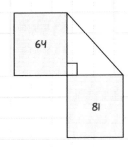

SHOW YOUR WORK

4. Fill in the missing values. ....^{2} + ...^{2} = c^2

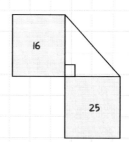

16

25

SHOW YOUR WORK

5. Fill in the missing values. ....^{2} + ...^{2} = c^2

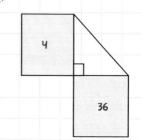

4

36

SHOW YOUR WORK

6. Fill in the missing values. .... + ... = c^2

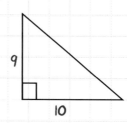

9

10

SHOW YOUR WORK

7. Fill in the missing values. .... + ... = c^2

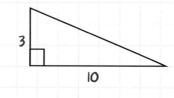

3

10

SHOW YOUR WORK

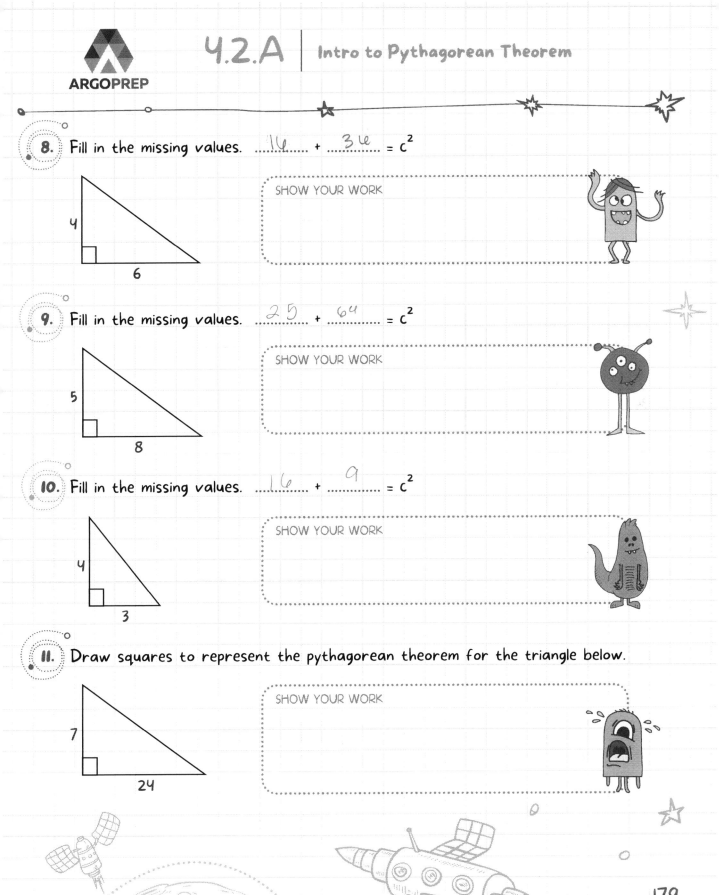

8. Fill in the missing values. ....16.... + ...36.... = c²

SHOW YOUR WORK

4

6

9. Fill in the missing values. ....25.... + ...64.... = c²

SHOW YOUR WORK

5

8

10. Fill in the missing values. ....16.... + ...9.... = c²

SHOW YOUR WORK

4

3

11. Draw squares to represent the pythagorean theorem for the triangle below.

SHOW YOUR WORK

7

24

12. Draw squares to represent the pythagorean theorem for the triangle below.

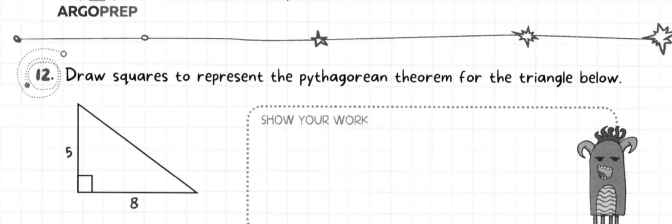

SHOW YOUR WORK

5

8

13. Draw squares to represent the pythagorean theorem for the triangle below.

SHOW YOUR WORK

3

10

14. Draw squares to represent the pythagorean theorem for the triangle below.

SHOW YOUR WORK

4

3

15. Draw squares to represent the pythagorean theorem for the triangle below.

SHOW YOUR WORK

7

24

ARGOPREP

Practice Questions

1. Calculate the length of the hypotenuse.

12

5

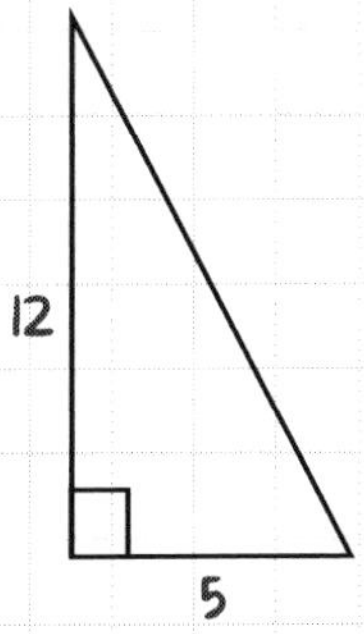

SHOW YOUR WORK

2. Calculate the length of the hypotenuse.

4

3

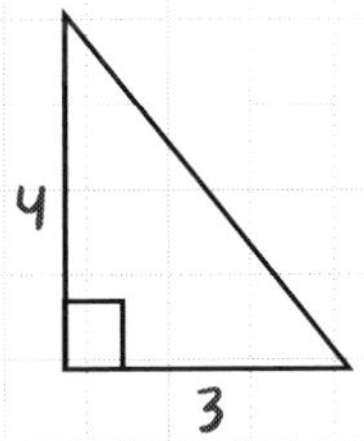

SHOW YOUR WORK

3. Calculate the length of the hypotenuse.

6

8

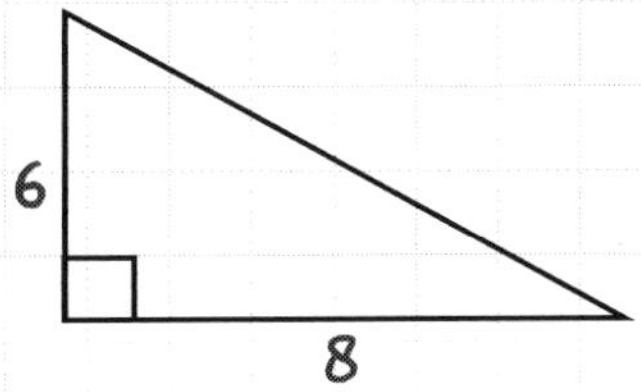

SHOW YOUR WORK

4. Calculate the length of the hypotenuse.

6

8

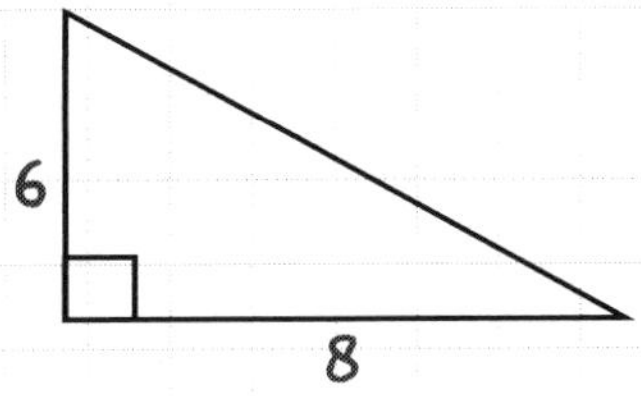

SHOW YOUR WORK

5. Calculate the length of the hypotenuse.

9
12

SHOW YOUR WORK

6. Calculate the length of the missing side.

20
12

SHOW YOUR WORK

7. Calculate the length of the missing side.

29
20

SHOW YOUR WORK

8. Calculate the length of the missing side.

30
24

SHOW YOUR WORK

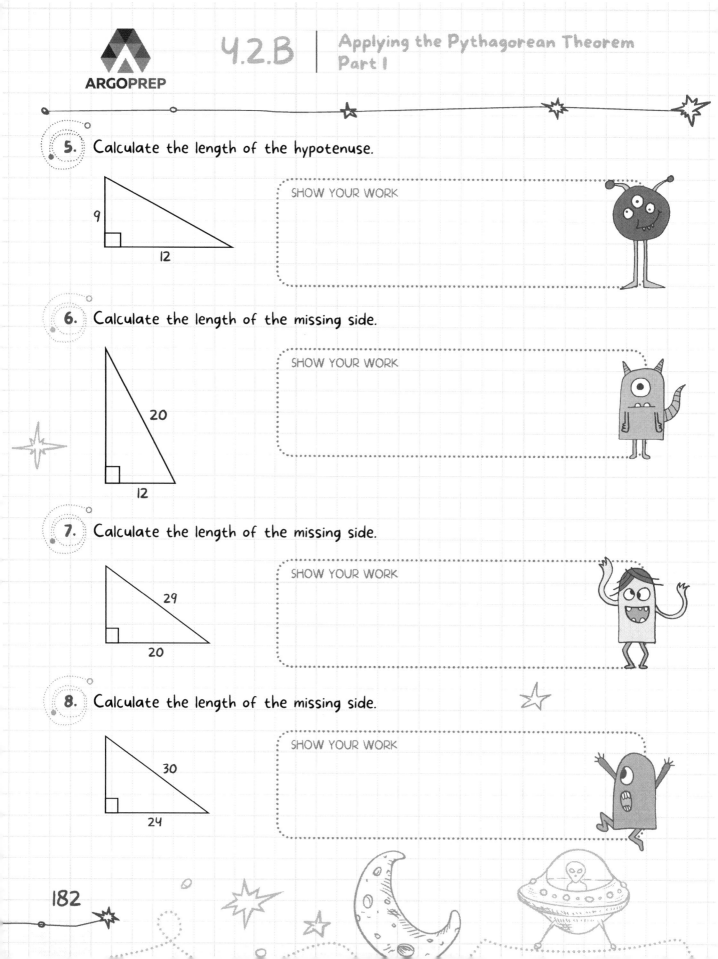

9. Calculate the length of the missing side.

25
24

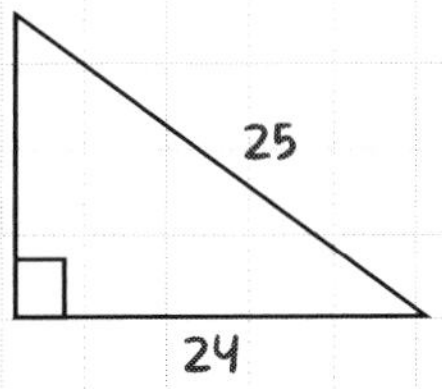

SHOW YOUR WORK

10. Calculate the length of the missing side.

34
30

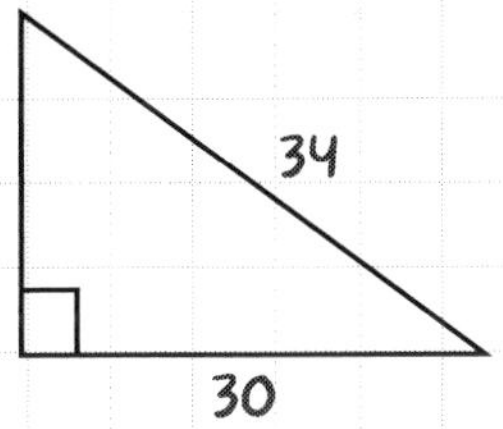

SHOW YOUR WORK

11. Solve for hypotenuse c

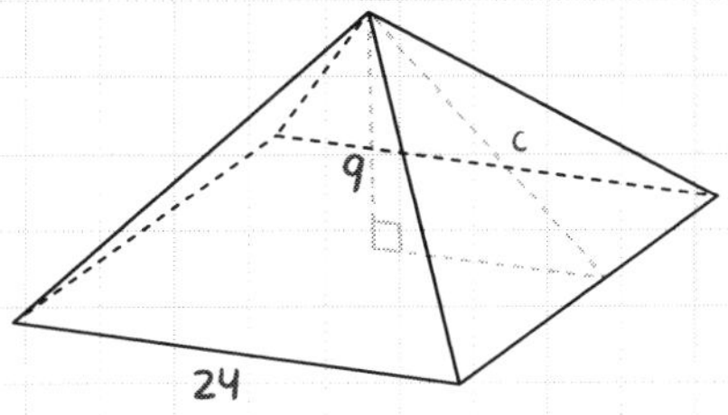

9
c
24

SHOW YOUR WORK

12. Solve for side a

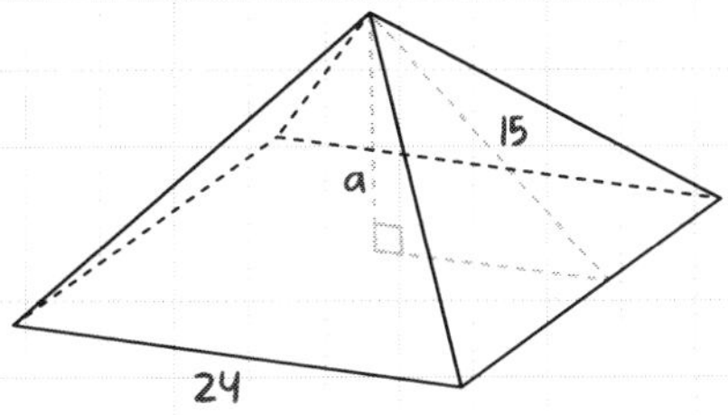

15
a
24

SHOW YOUR WORK

13. Solve for hypotenuse c

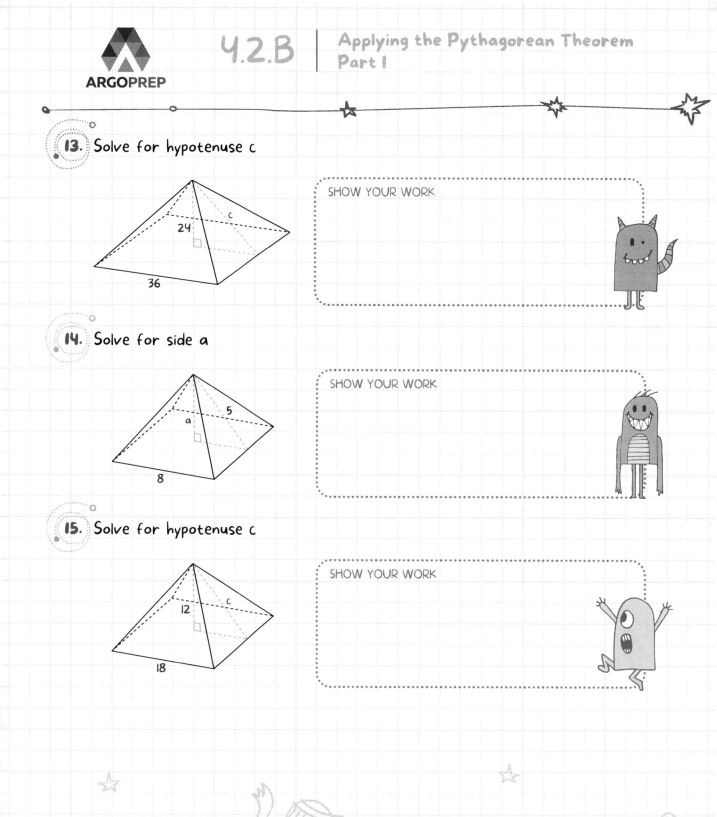

SHOW YOUR WORK

14. Solve for side a

SHOW YOUR WORK

15. Solve for hypotenuse c

SHOW YOUR WORK

We can use the pythagorean theorem to find the distance between two points on a coordinate plane. For example...

Use the pythagorean theorem to find the distance between Point A and Point B

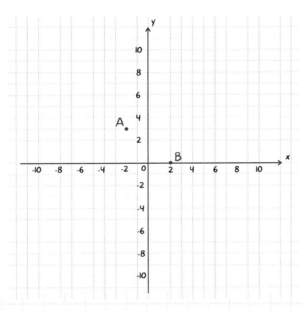

Step 1: Connect the two points with a straight line.

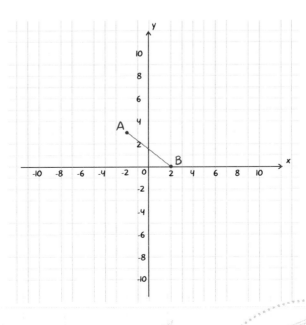

185

Step 2: Create a right triangle using the x-axis and y-axis.

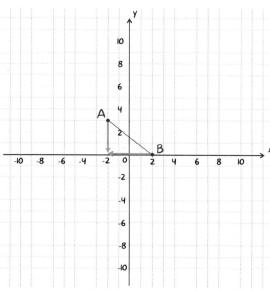

Step 3: Calculate the missing side length using the Pythagorean Theorem.

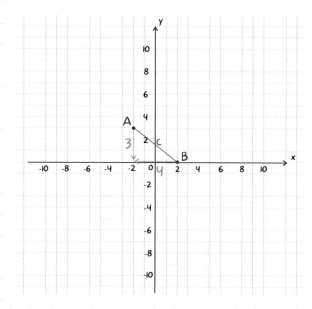

$$a^2 + b^2 = c^2$$

$$(3)^2 + (4)^2 = c^2$$

$$9 + 16 + c^2$$

$$25 = c^2$$

$$\sqrt{25} = c$$

$$5 = c$$

Use the coordinate plane below to answer questions 1 - 3.

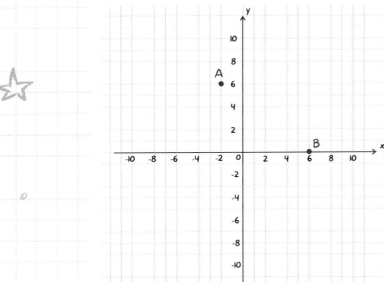

1. Use lines to create a right triangle.

    SHOW YOUR WORK

2. What are the lengths of the two straight sides?

    SHOW YOUR WORK

3. What is the length of the hypotenuse?

    SHOW YOUR WORK

Use the coordinate plane below to answer questions 4 - 6.

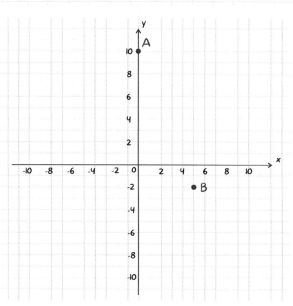

4. Use lines to create a right triangle.

SHOW YOUR WORK

5. What are the lengths of the two straight sides?

SHOW YOUR WORK

6. What is the length of the hypotenuse?

SHOW YOUR WORK

Use the coordinate plane below to answer questions 7 - 9.

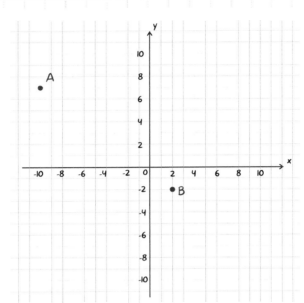

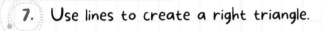

7. Use lines to create a right triangle.

> SHOW YOUR WORK

8. What are the lengths of the two straight sides?

> SHOW YOUR WORK

9. What is the length of the hypotenuse?

> SHOW YOUR WORK

Use the coordinate plane below to answer questions 10 - 12.

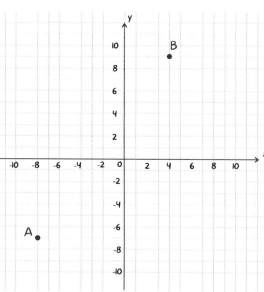

10. Use lines to create a right triangle.

> SHOW YOUR WORK

11. What are the lengths of the two straight sides?

> SHOW YOUR WORK

12. What is the length of the hypotenuse?

> SHOW YOUR WORK

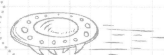

Use the coordinate plane below to answer questions 13 - 15.

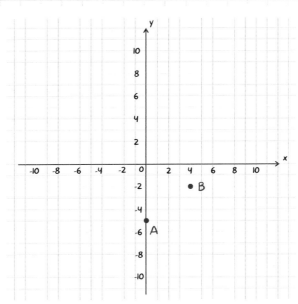

13. Use lines to create a right triangle.

> SHOW YOUR WORK

14. What are the lengths of the two straight sides?

> SHOW YOUR WORK

15. What is the length of the hypotenuse?

> SHOW YOUR WORK

CONES

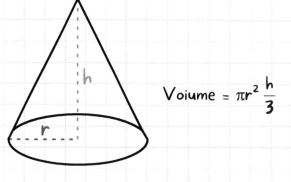

$$\text{Voiume} = \pi r^2 \frac{h}{3}$$

CYLINDERS

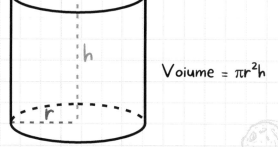

$$\text{Voiume} = \pi r^2 h$$

SPHERES

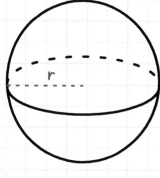

$$\text{Voiume} = \frac{4}{3}\pi r^3$$

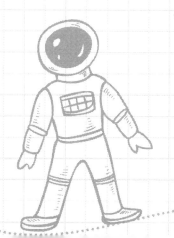

Practice Questions

1. Find the volume of the cone.

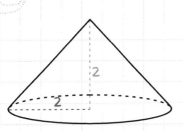

SHOW YOUR WORK

2. Find the volume of the cone.

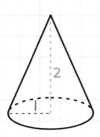

SHOW YOUR WORK

3. Find the volume of the cone.

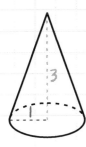

SHOW YOUR WORK

4. Find the volume of the cone.

SHOW YOUR WORK

5. Find the volume of the cone.

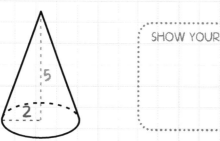

SHOW YOUR WORK

6. Find the volume of the cylinder.

SHOW YOUR WORK

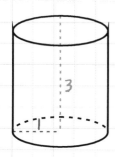

7. Find the volume of the cylinder.

SHOW YOUR WORK

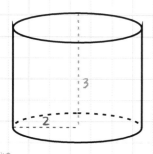

8. Find the volume of the cylinder.

SHOW YOUR WORK

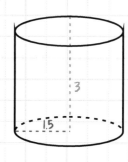

9. Find the volume of the cylinder.

2.5

2

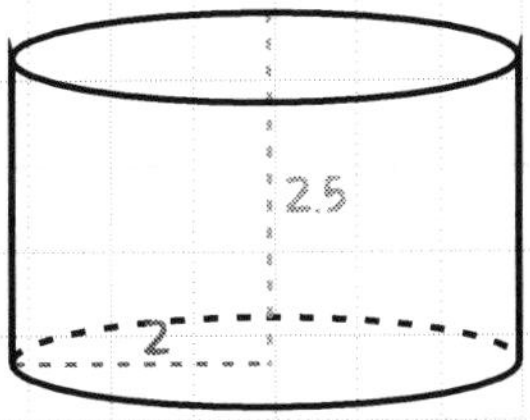

SHOW YOUR WORK

10. Find the volume of the cylinder.

5

2

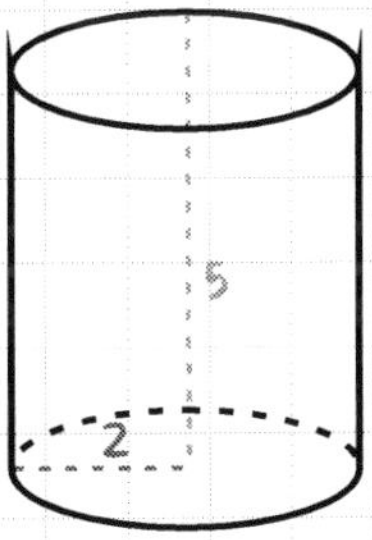

SHOW YOUR WORK

11. Find the volume of the sphere.

9

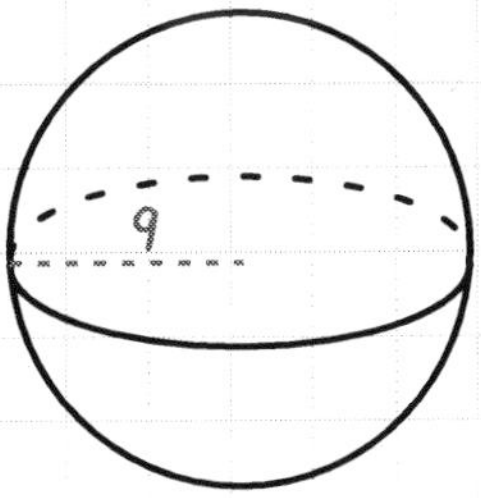

SHOW YOUR WORK

12. Find the volume of the sphere.

2

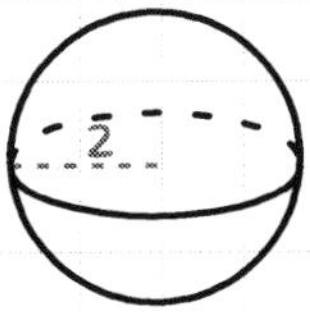

SHOW YOUR WORK

13. Find the volume of the sphere.

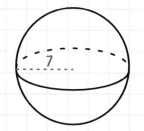

7

SHOW YOUR WORK

14. Find the volume of the sphere.

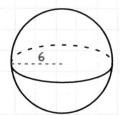

6

SHOW YOUR WORK

15. Find the volume of the sphere.

2.5

SHOW YOUR WORK

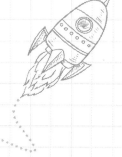

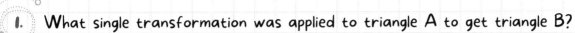

1. What single transformation was applied to triangle A to get triangle B?

A. Rotation   **B.** Reflection   **C.** Translation

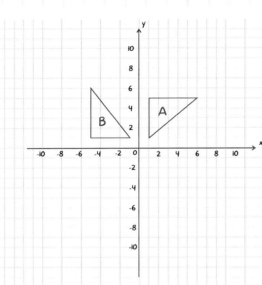

SHOW YOUR WORK

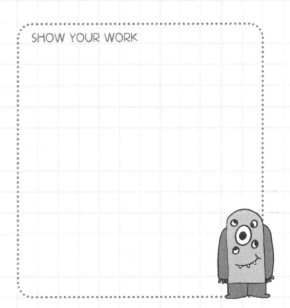

2. What single transformation was applied to rectangle A to get rectangle B?

A. Rotation   **B.** Reflection   **C.** Translation

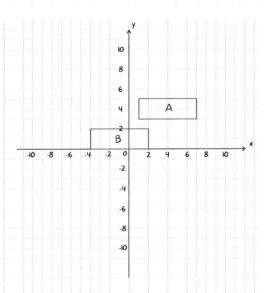

SHOW YOUR WORK

3. What single transformation was applied to triangle A to get triangle B?

A. Rotation   **B.** Reflection   **C.** Translation

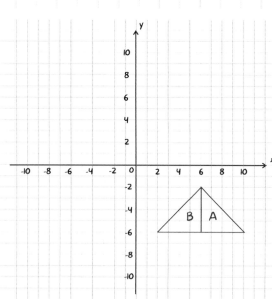

SHOW YOUR WORK

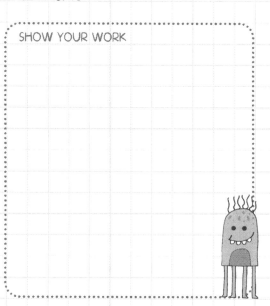

4. Plot the image of Point B under a reflection across line *d*.

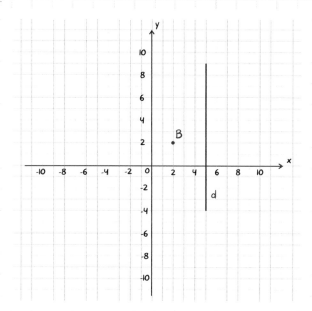

SHOW YOUR WORK

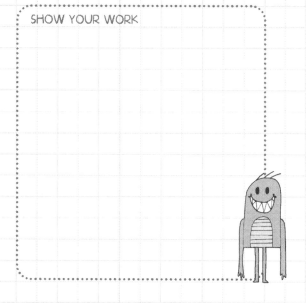

5. Draw the line of reflection for △ ABC onto △ A'B'C'.

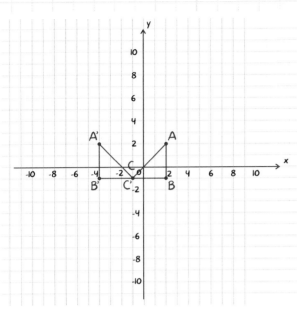

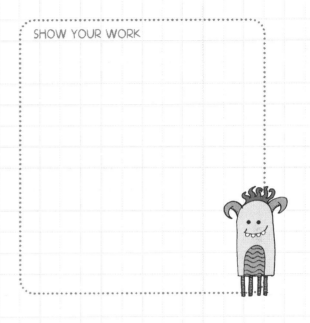

SHOW YOUR WORK

6. Point B' is the image of Point B under a rotation around the origin. Determine the angle of rotation.

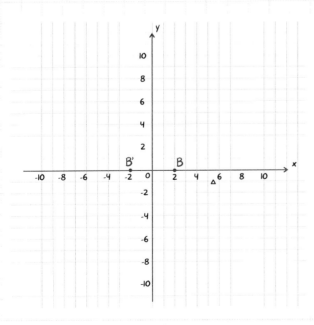

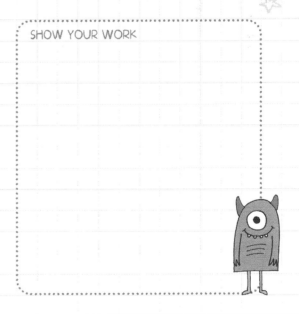

SHOW YOUR WORK

7. Point A' (6, 5) represents Point A (9, 10) under a translation. Point A' represents a translation by **3** units to the .... and **5** units ....

Rectangle ABCD is rotated **90°** clockwise around the origin to form rectangle EFGH. Use the rectangles to answer questions **8 - 9.**

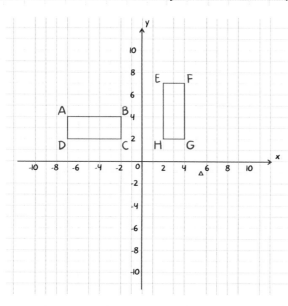

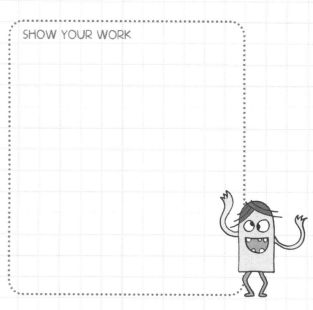

SHOW YOUR WORK

8. Which statement is true about the relationship between rectangle ABCD and rectangle EFGH?

A. $\overline{AB} \cong \overline{HG}$

B. $\overline{DA} \cong \overline{EF}$

C. $\overline{CD} \cong \overline{FG}$

D. $\overline{BC} \cong \overline{EF}$

SHOW YOUR WORK

9. Which statement is true about the relationship between rectangle ABCD and rectangle EFGH?

A. $\overline{AB} \cong \overline{FG}$

B. $\overline{GH} \cong \overline{CD}$

C. $\overline{DA} \cong \overline{FE}$

D. $\overline{CD} \cong \overline{HE}$

SHOW YOUR WORK

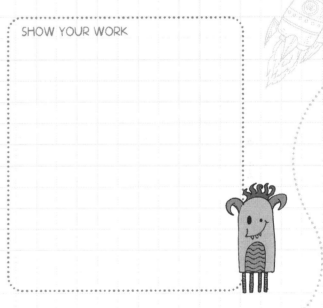

10. Plot the image of point A under dilation about the origin with a scale of 2.

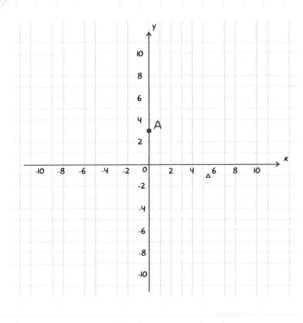

SHOW YOUR WORK

11. Plot the image of point A under dilation about the origin with a scale of $\frac{1}{2}$.

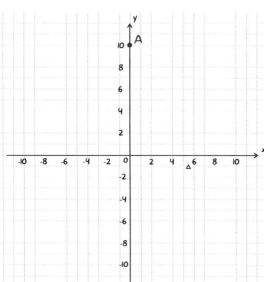

SHOW YOUR WORK

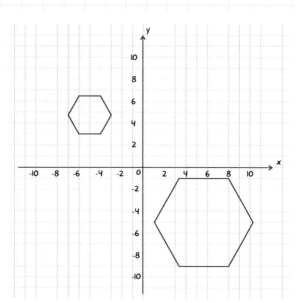

12. Use the coordinate plane to determine if the shapes are similar.

SHOW YOUR WORK

13. Explain why the figures are/aren't similar.

SHOW YOUR WORK

14. Find the volume of the cone.

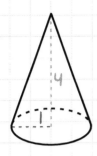

SHOW YOUR WORK

4

1

15. Find the volume of the sphere.

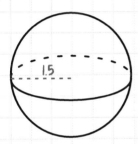

1.5

SHOW YOUR WORK

16. Find the volume of the cylinder.

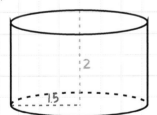

2

7.5

SHOW YOUR WORK

17. Fill in the missing values.   ....^{2} + ...^{2} = c^2

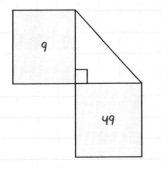

9

49

SHOW YOUR WORK

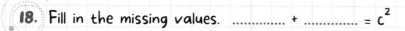

18. Fill in the missing values. .... + ... = c^2

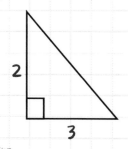

2

3

SHOW YOUR WORK

19. Solve for side a.

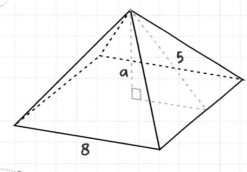

5

a

8

SHOW YOUR WORK

20. What is the length of side AB?

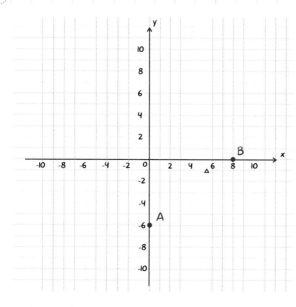

SHOW YOUR WORK

NOTES

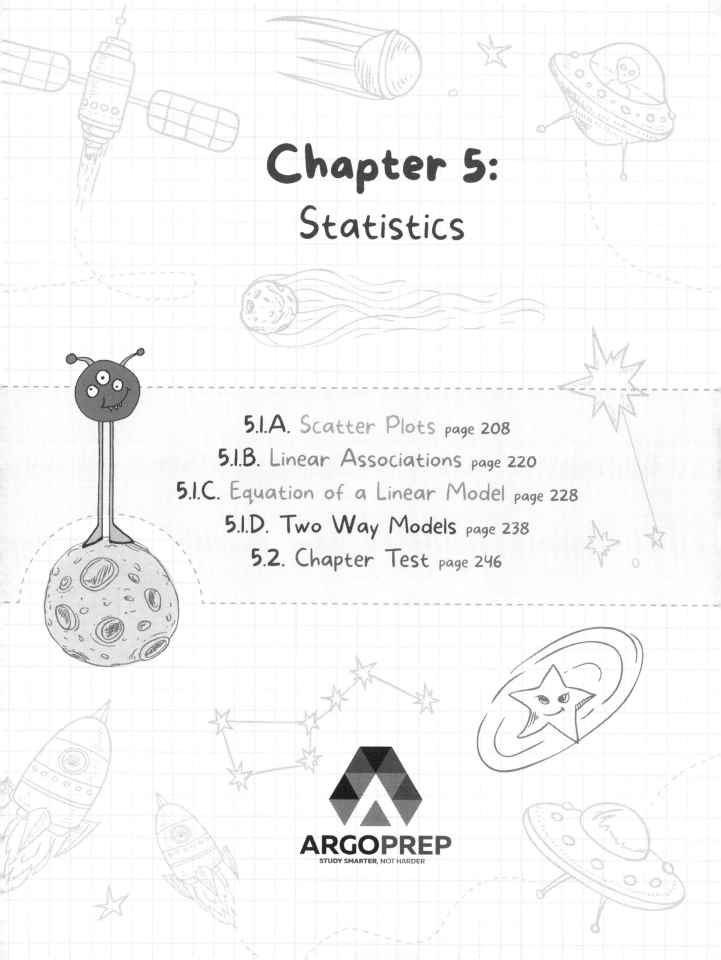

Chapter 5:
Statistics

5.1.A. Scatter Plots page 208
5.1.B. Linear Associations page 220
5.1.C. Equation of a Linear Model page 228
5.1.D. Two Way Models page 238
5.2. Chapter Test page 246

ARGOPREP
STUDY SMARTER, NOT HARDER

We can use scatter plots to analyze patterns between two quantities.

Plot the data using a scatter plot. What is the association between the two variables?

Student	Jim	Jan	Jill	John	Joey
Test Score	90	70	80	75	100
Hours Studied	4	2	3	2	6

Step 1: Plot the Data

Plot the data on a coordinate plane, using the x-axis for one variable and the y-axis for another. For the example above, we can set the y-axis to represent test scores and the x-axis to represent the number of hours studied.

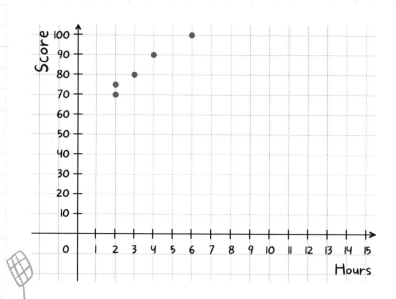

<u>Step 2:</u> Analyze the Data

A scatter plot helps you quickly see whether or not there is an association between the two variables. Possible associations include:

POSITIVE OR NEGATIVE ASSOCIATION

Positive

High values of x are associated with high values of y

Negative

Low values of x are associated with high values of y

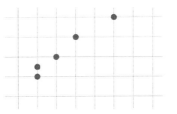
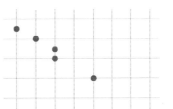

LINEAR OR NONLINEAR ASSOCIATION

Linear

The data can be modeled as a straight line

Nonlinear

The data cannot be modeled as a straight line

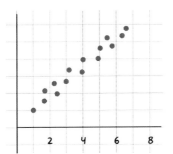
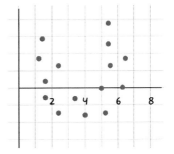

CLUSTERING OR OUTLIERS

Clustering

Grouping of data points

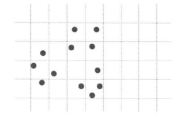

Outliers

Data points that are far away from rest of the data

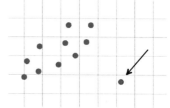

NOTES

Practice Questions

Use the table below to answer questions 1-3.

Grade Level	First	Second	Third	Fourth	Fifth
Girl Students	12	13	14	14	11
Boy Students	7	13	12	10	12

1. Plot the data using a scatter plot.

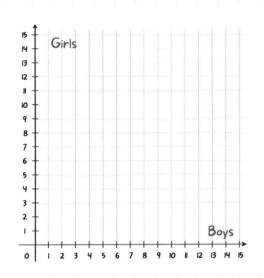

SHOW YOUR WORK

2. What is the association between the two variables?

SHOW YOUR WORK

211

3. What prediction could be made based on the scatter plot?

A. The number of girls in each class is always greater than the number of boys

B. The number of boys in each class is always greater than the number of girls

C. None of the above

SHOW YOUR WORK

Use the table below to answer questions 4-6.

Student	Hannah	Rachel	Eric	Juan
Height	3.5 ft	4 ft	5 ft	6 ft
Shoe size	4	5.5	8	10

4. Plot the data using a scatter plot.

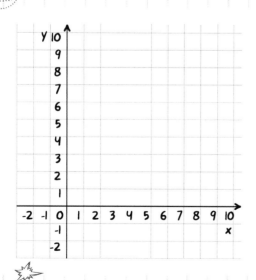

SHOW YOUR WORK

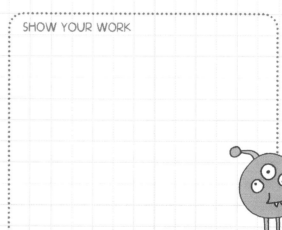

5. What is the association between the two variables?

> SHOW YOUR WORK

6. What prediction could be made based on the scatter plot?

A. Shorter students have bigger feet

B. Taller students have bigger feet

C. None of the above

> SHOW YOUR WORK

Use the table below to answer questions 7-9.

Age (years)	5	6	7	8	9	10
Daily Screen Time (hours)	.5	2	1	3.5	3	4

7. Plot the data using a scatter plot.

SHOW YOUR WORK

8. What is the association between the two variables?

SHOW YOUR WORK

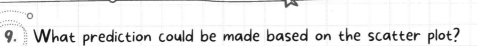

9. What prediction could be made based on the scatter plot?

A. The age group with the least screen time is five

B. The age group with the most screen time is eight

C. None of the above

SHOW YOUR WORK

Use the table below to answer questions 10-12.

Age	Miles Walked
20	8
25	7.5
30	6
35	7
40	6
50	5
55	4
60	3
70	1.5

10. Plot the data using a scatter plot.

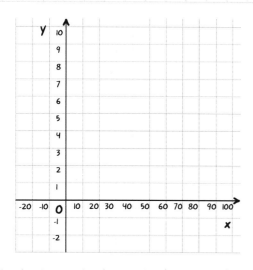

SHOW YOUR WORK

11. What is the association between the two variables?

SHOW YOUR WORK

12. What prediction could be made based on the scatter plot?

A. Younger people walked more

B. Older people walked more

C. None of the above

SHOW YOUR WORK

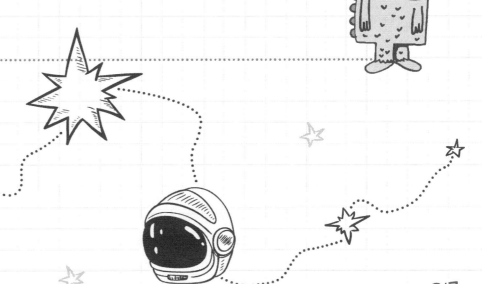

Use the table below to answer questions 13-15.

Awards	1	2	3	4	8
Practice Time (hours)	0	2	4	6	8

13. Plot the data using a scatter plot.

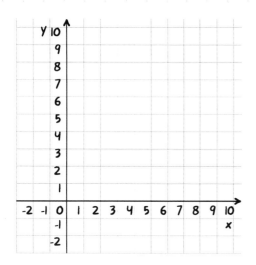

SHOW YOUR WORK

14. What is the association between the two variables?

SHOW YOUR WORK

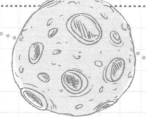

ARGOPREP

15. What prediction could be made based on the scatter plot?

A. There is a cluster

B. There is an outlier

C. None of the above

SHOW YOUR WORK

NOTES

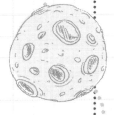

We can use a **line of best fit** to better analyze scatter plots with linear associations.

The **line of best fit** is a straight line used to represent linear associations on a scatter plot. The line is estimated, but should be drawn as close to all the data points as possible, with as many dots above the line as there are below the line.

For example...

Draw the line of best fit for the graph below. Explain why your answer is correct.

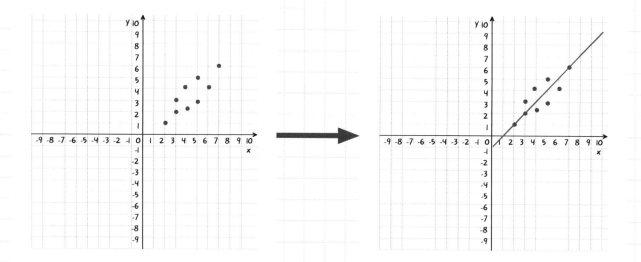

The line is as close to the points as possible, with three points above the line and three points below the line. Based on the **line of best fit** we can predict that when $x = 8$, y will equal 7.

Practice Questions

1. Which line represents the *line of best fit*? Explain your answer.

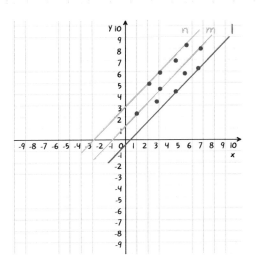

SHOW YOUR WORK

2. Which line represents the *line of best fit*? Explain your answer.

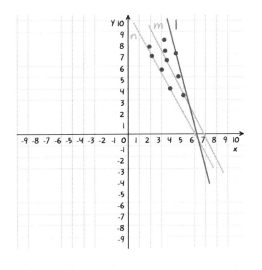

SHOW YOUR WORK

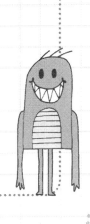

3. Which line represents the *line of best fit?* Explain your answer.

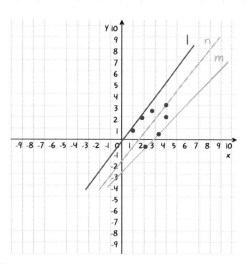

SHOW YOUR WORK

4. Which line represents the *line of best fit?* Explain your answer.

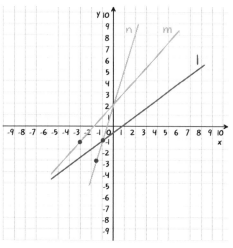

SHOW YOUR WORK

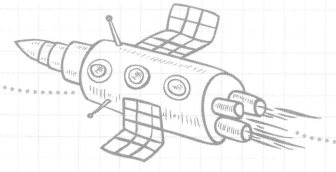

5. Which line represents the line of best fit? Explain your answer.

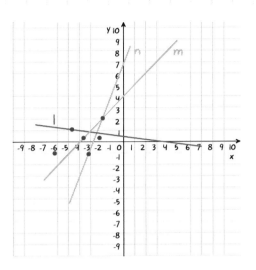

6. Draw the line of best fit for the scatter plot below.

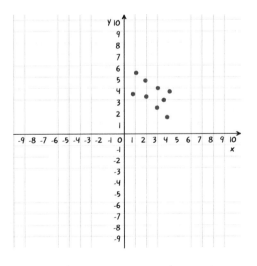

SHOW YOUR WORK

7. Draw the line of best fit for the scatter plot below.

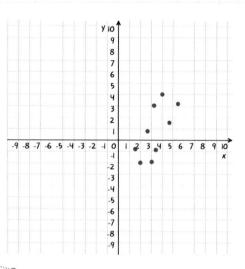

SHOW YOUR WORK

8. Draw the line of best fit for the scatter plot below.

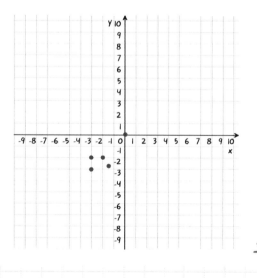

SHOW YOUR WORK

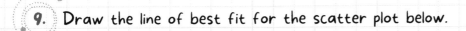

9. Draw the line of best fit for the scatter plot below.

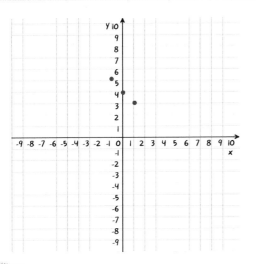

SHOW YOUR WORK

10. Draw the line of best fit for the scatter plot below.

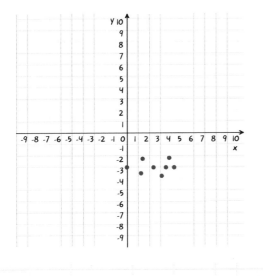

SHOW YOUR WORK

Use the table below to answer questions 11-15

Weeks Worked	2	4	5	6	7	8	10
Vacation Days Earned	1	2	3.5	6	6	7	9

11. Create a scatter plot to represent relationship between weeks worked and vacation days earned.

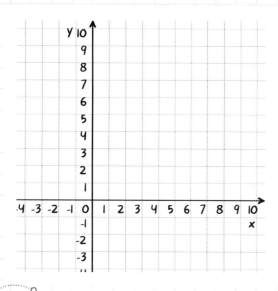

SHOW YOUR WORK

12. The variables have a _____ association.

A. Positive

B. Negative

SHOW YOUR WORK

226

13. Draw the line of best fit for the scatter plot.

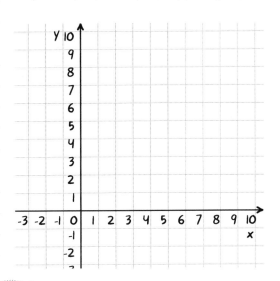

SHOW YOUR WORK

14. Based on the line of best fit, how many vacation days does someone earn at **3 weeks?**

A. 1

B. 1.5

C. 2

D. 2.5

SHOW YOUR WORK

15. What other observations can you make based on the line of best fit?

SHOW YOUR WORK

We can use slope-intercept form **(y = mx+ b)** to write equations for linear models. The slope (m) represents the rate of change. The y-intercept (b) represents the value of y when x is zero.

The graph below shows the relationship between hours spent studying for the math exam and hours spent studying for the reading exam for students in Mr. Roby's class.

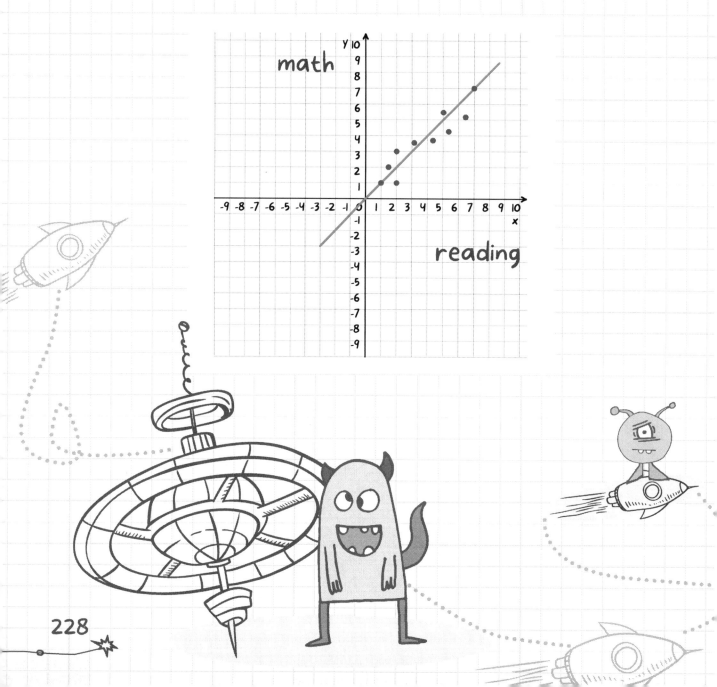

Y-INTERCEPT

We can see that the **line of best fit** crosses the y-axis at 0. Therefore, the y-intercept is 0.

This tells us that students who studied 0 hours of reading also studied 0 hours of math.

SLOPE

$$\text{Slope} = \frac{(y^2 - y^1)}{(x^2 - x^1)}$$

We can select any two points on the line of best fit to determine slope. Let's use $(1, 1)$ and $(7, 7)$

$$\text{Slope} = \frac{(7 - 1)}{(7 - 1)} = 1$$

This tells us that an additional hour of reading study is associated with an additional hour of math study.

LINEAR EQUATION

Now that we know the slope and y-intercept, we can write a linear equation for the model.

$$y = (1)x + 0 \quad \text{or} \quad y = x$$

Based on this equation, Mr. Roby could make the prediction that his students spent the same amount of time for math as they did reading.

Practice Questions

The graph below shows the relationship between goals scored and years on the soccer team. The line of best fit is given. Use the graph to answer questions 1 – 5.

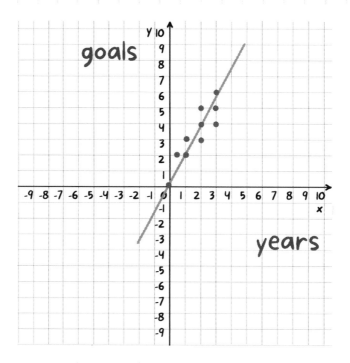

1. What is the y-intercept of the best fitting line?

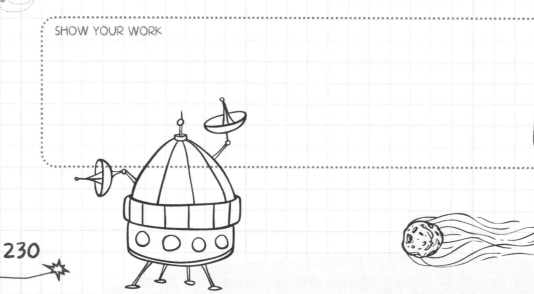

SHOW YOUR WORK

2. What is the slope of the best fitting line?

SHOW YOUR WORK

3. Write a linear equation to represent the model

SHOW YOUR WORK

4. According to the line of best fit, which statement best describes the relationship between years on the soccer team and goals scored?

A. Students who have been on the team the longest score the fewest number of goals

B. Students score 2 goals for every year they've been on the team

C. None of the above

SHOW YOUR WORK

5. Which of the following statements is a valid prediction based on the model?

A. If a student stays on the team for 4 years, she can expect to score 8 goals

B. If a student stays on the team for 4 years, she can expect to score 4 goals

C. None of the above

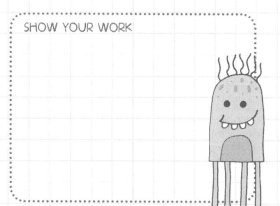

SHOW YOUR WORK

The graph below shows the relationship between number of cookies eaten at the party and bedtime. The line of best fit is given. Use the graph to answer questions 6 – 10.

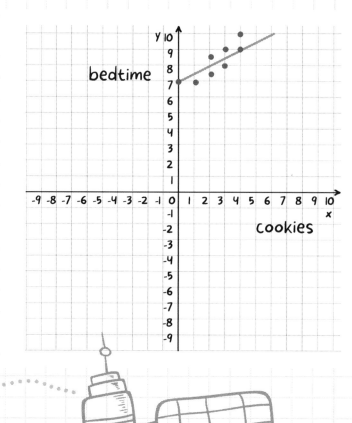

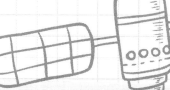

6. What is the y-intercept of the best fitting line?

SHOW YOUR WORK

7. What is the slope of the best fitting line?

SHOW YOUR WORK

8. Write a linear equation to represent the model.

SHOW YOUR WORK

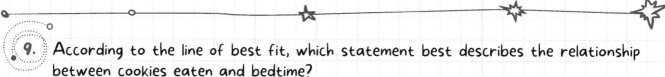

9. According to the line of best fit, which statement best describes the relationship between cookies eaten and bedtime?

    A. The number of cookies eaten has no association with bedtime

    B. The number of cookies eaten has a positive association with bedtime

    C. The number of cookies eaten has a negative association with bedtime

SHOW YOUR WORK

10. Which statement best describes the rate of change?

    A. Bedtime increases by one hour for every one cookie eaten

    B. Bedtime increases by one hour for every two cookies eaten

    C. Bedtime increases by two hours for every one cookie eaten

SHOW YOUR WORK

The graph below shows the relationship between gallons of gas and miles driven. The line of best fit is given. Use the graph to answer questions 11 – 15.

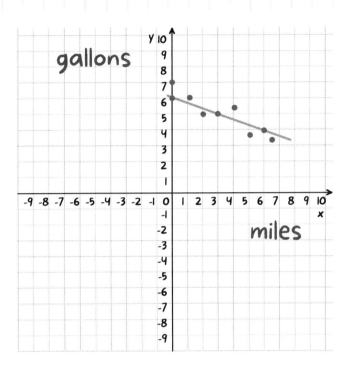

11. What is the y-intercept of the best fitting line?

SHOW YOUR WORK

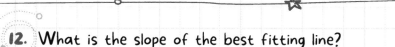

12. What is the slope of the best fitting line?

SHOW YOUR WORK

13. Write a linear equation to represent the model.

SHOW YOUR WORK

14. According to the line of best fit, which statement best describes the relationship between miles driven and gallons?

A. The gallons of gas has no association with miles driven.

B. The gallons of gas has a positive association with miles driven.

C. The gallons of gas has a negative association with miles driven.

SHOW YOUR WORK

15. At what mile will the gas run out?

SHOW YOUR WORK

NOTES

A two-way table shows data classified in two ways. For example...

Mrs. O'Dor asked her students whether they prefer chocolate or vanilla ice cream. The table below shows the responses based on gender.

	Male	Female
Chocolate Ice Cream	9	6
Vanilla Ice Cream	4	5

The first thing we notice is that there are two variables (gender and ice cream flavor). We can use the information to answer a variety of questions.

How many students like chocolate ice cream?

To determine the number of students who like chocolate ice cream we need to read across the chocolate ice cream row and add the numbers together.

	Male	Female
Chocolate Ice Cream	9	6
Vanilla Ice Cream	4	5

9 + 6 = 15

15 students prefer chocolate ice cream to vanilla ice cream.

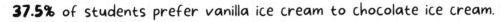

What percentage of students like vanilla ice cream?

First, calculate the number of students who like vanilla ice cream.

	Male	Female
Chocolate Ice Cream	9	6
Vanilla Ice Cream	4	5

$$4 + 5 = 9$$

Next, calculate the total number of students surveyed.

	Male	Female
Chocolate Ice Cream	9	6
Vanilla Ice Cream	4	5

$$9 + 6 + 4 + 5 = 24$$

Finally, determine the percent.

9 out of 24

$$\frac{9}{24} = .375 \times 10 = 37.5$$

37.5% of students prefer vanilla ice cream to chocolate ice cream.

Practice Questions

Mr. Walker asked his middle school students which color they preferred, pink or blue. He organized his data by gender using the table below. Use the table to answer questions 1 – 5.

Preference	Male	Female
Pink	12	18
Blue	14	6

1. How many students were surveyed?

SHOW YOUR WORK

2. What percent of students prefer the color pink?

SHOW YOUR WORK

3. What percent of female students prefer the color blue?

SHOW YOUR WORK

4. How many students prefer the color blue?

SHOW YOUR WORK

5. How many males were surveyed?

SHOW YOUR WORK

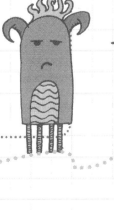

Mrs. Pegram asked all of her coworkers if they prefer chocolate or flowers on Valentine's Day. She sorted her data by age using the table below. Use the table to answer questions **6 – 10**.

Preference	Younger than 25	Older than 25
Chocolate	9	23
Flowers	31	17

6. How many people answered the survey?

SHOW YOUR WORK

7. What percent of Mrs. Pegram's coworkers are older than 25?

SHOW YOUR WORK

8. What percent of coworkers prefer flowers?

SHOW YOUR WORK

9. How many of Mrs. Pegram's coworkers prefer chocolate?

SHOW YOUR WORK

10. How many of Mrs. Pegram's coworkers are younger than 25?

SHOW YOUR WORK

Baylee surveyed her class about which candy they prefer on Halloween. Use the information below to answer questions 11 - 15.

 50 students were surveyed

 Half of the students preferred chocolate candy

 20% of the students who preferred chocolate were female, the rest were male

 10 of the students who preferred sour candy were male

11. How many students prefer chocolate candy?

SHOW YOUR WORK

12. How many female students preferred chocolate?

SHOW YOUR WORK

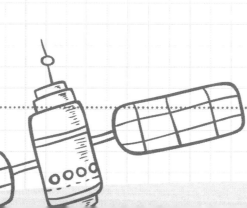

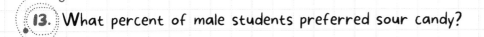

13. What percent of male students preferred sour candy?

SHOW YOUR WORK

14. How many female students were surveyed?

SHOW YOUR WORK

15. Create a two way table for the data.

SHOW YOUR WORK

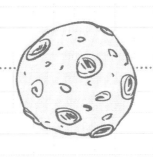
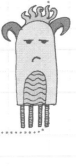

1. Which of the following scatter plots shows a negative association?

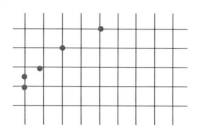

A.

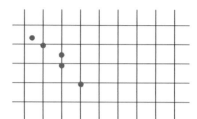

B.

SHOW YOUR WORK

2. Which of the following scatter plots shows a linear association?

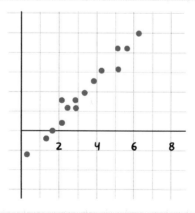

A.

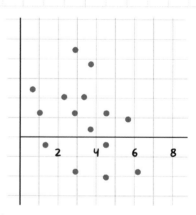

B.

SHOW YOUR WORK

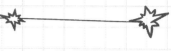

3. Which of the following scatter plots contains an outlier?

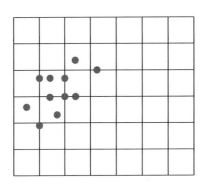

A.

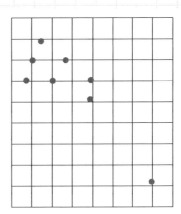

B.

SHOW YOUR WORK

The table below shows the relationship between miles walked for a school fundraiser and student age. Use the table to answer questions 4 – 7.

Age	5	5	5	6	6	6	7	7	7	8	8	8	9	9	9	10	10	10	10
Miles Walked	0	1	2	2	4	5	2	2.5	4	4	4.5	6	6	7	8	8	9	9.5	7

4. Plot the data using a scatter plot.

SHOW YOUR WORK

5. What is the association between the two variables?

SHOW YOUR WORK

6. Draw the line of best fit for the scatter plot.

SHOW YOUR WORK

7. What prediction could be made based on the scatter plot?

A. There is a cluster

B. There is an outlier

C. None of the above

The graph below shows the relationship between gallons of gas and miles driven. The line of best fit is given. Use the graph to answer questions 8 – 13.

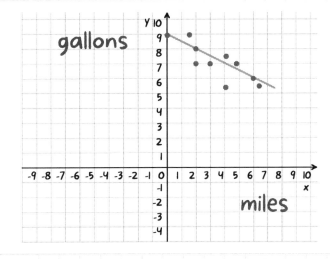

8. What is the association between the two variables?

SHOW YOUR WORK

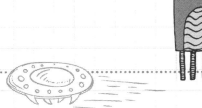

9. What is the y-intercept of the best fitting line?

SHOW YOUR WORK

10. What is the slope of the best fitting line?

SHOW YOUR WORK

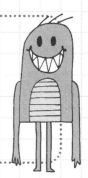

11. Write a linear equation to represent the model.

SHOW YOUR WORK

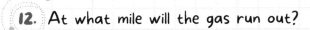

12. At what mile will the gas run out?

SHOW YOUR WORK

13. Which of the following statements is a valid prediction?

A. Every two miles the gas decreases by **2** gallons

B. Every two miles the gas decreases by 1 gallon

C. None of the above

SHOW YOUR WORK

ARGOPREP

Use the table below to answer questions 14 – 15.

Preference	Moms	Dads
Golf	5	10
Tennis	7	3

14. What percent of moms prefer tennis?

SHOW YOUR WORK

15. How many people preferred golf?

SHOW YOUR WORK

NOTES

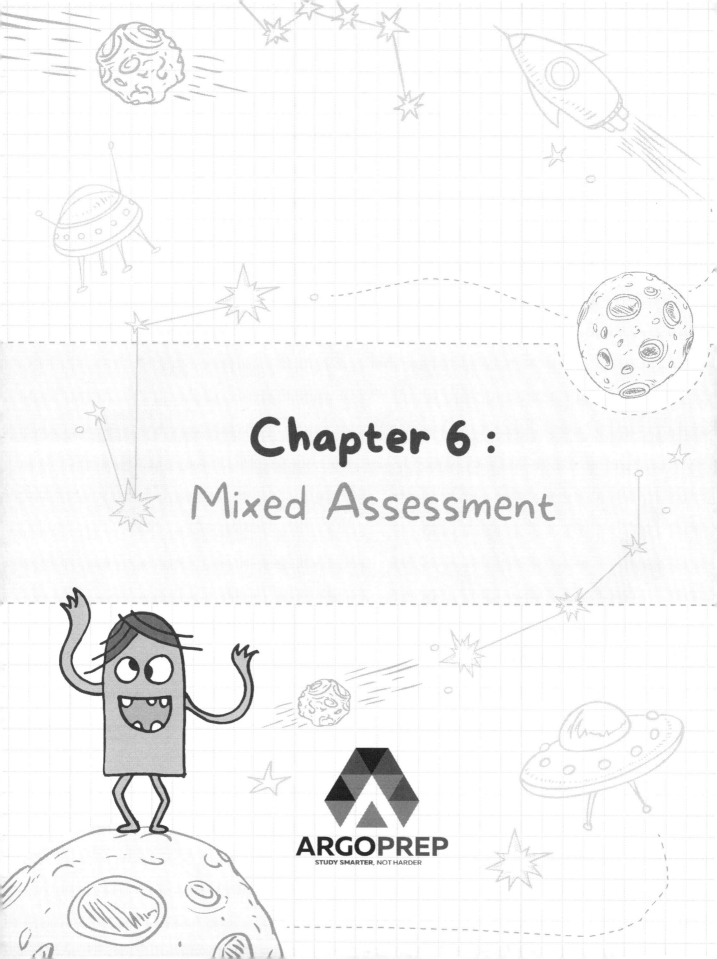

Chapter 6 :
Mixed Assessment

Determine whether numbers are rational or irrational for questions 1 - 10.

1. -5

A. rational

B. irrational

SHOW YOUR WORK

2. $\dfrac{6}{2}$

A. rational

B. irrational

SHOW YOUR WORK

3. π

A. rational

B. irrational

SHOW YOUR WORK

4. $\sqrt{49}$

A. rational

B. irrational

SHOW YOUR WORK

5. $\sqrt{8}$

A. rational

B. irrational

SHOW YOUR WORK

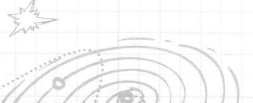

6. $\sqrt{\dfrac{4}{2}}$

A. rational

B. irrational

SHOW YOUR WORK

7. $\dfrac{7}{2}$

A. rational

B. irrational

SHOW YOUR WORK

8. 4π

A. rational

B. irrational

SHOW YOUR WORK

9. -7.2

A. rational

B. irrational

SHOW YOUR WORK

10. 1,457

A. rational

B. irrational

SHOW YOUR WORK

11. Order the numbers below from least to greatest without using a calculator.

$\sqrt{90}$, 11, 9, 10

SHOW YOUR WORK

12. Order the numbers below from least to greatest without using a calculator.

-5, $\sqrt{54}$, 7, 10

SHOW YOUR WORK

13. Order the numbers below from least to greatest without using a calculator.

$\sqrt{5}$, 3, 4

SHOW YOUR WORK

14. Complete the inequality without using a calculator.

$\sqrt{40}$ 7

SHOW YOUR WORK

15. Complete the inequality without using a calculator.

6 .... $\sqrt{30}$

SHOW YOUR WORK

16. Complete the inequality without using a calculator.

8 .... $\sqrt{64}$

SHOW YOUR WORK

17. Use whole numbers to create an inequality for the irrational number.

.... < **2π - 5** < ....

SHOW YOUR WORK

18. Use whole numbers to create an inequality for the irrational number.

.... < $\sqrt{122}$ < ....

SHOW YOUR WORK

19. Plot $\sqrt{5}$ on the number line.

```
 ├────┼────┼────┼────┼────┼────┼────┼────┼────┼────►
 0    2    4    6    8    10
```

SHOW YOUR WORK

20. Plot $\frac{1}{2}\pi$ on the number line.

```
 ├────┼────┼────┼────┼────┼────┼────┼────┼────┼────►
 0    2    4    6    8    10
```

SHOW YOUR WORK

Use the scenario below to answer questions 21 - 23.

The average person uses **60** gallons of water each day. The city of New York uses 1,200,000,000 gallons of drinking water each day.

21. Which of the following is the best approximation for the amount of water New York uses every day?

    A. 1.2×10^9

    SHOW YOUR WORK

    B. 12×10^9

22. Which of the following is the best approximation for the amount of water the average person uses per day?

    A. 6×10^2

    SHOW YOUR WORK

    B. 6×10^1

23. The amount of water used by New York City is approximately .... times more than the amount of water the average person uses per day.

SHOW YOUR WORK

24. $(8 \times 10^3) + 8,500 =$ .... Write your answer in scientific notation.

SHOW YOUR WORK

25. $(2.5 \times 10^{-1}) + .05 = $ .... Write your answer in scientific notation.

SHOW YOUR WORK

26. $(1.75 \times 10^4) - (7.5 \times 10^3) = $ .... Write your answer in scientific notation.

SHOW YOUR WORK

27. $4,525 - (5.25 \times 10^2) = $ .... Write your answer in scientific notation.

SHOW YOUR WORK

28. The equation $18x + 15 = 3(6x + 5)$ has...

A. One Solution

B. No Solution

C. Many Solutions

SHOW YOUR WORK

29. The equation $4x + 2 = 3x + x + 5 - 3$ has...

A. One Solution

B. No Solution

C. Many Solutions

SHOW YOUR WORK

30. The equation $30x - 6 = 15x + 3$ has...

A. One Solution

B. No Solution

C. Many Solutions

SHOW YOUR WORK

31. Is the representation below a function? Explain your answer.

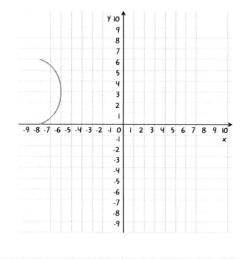

SHOW YOUR WORK

32. Is the representation below a function? Explain your answer.

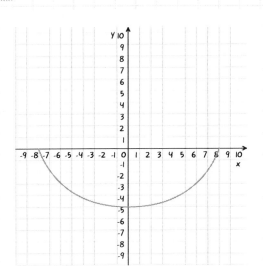

SHOW YOUR WORK

33. Which set of ordered pairs does <u>not</u> represent a function?

A. (0, 1), (2, -3), (4, 1), (6,-3)

B. (1,0), (-3,2), (1,4), (-3, 6)

SHOW YOUR WORK

34. Which set of ordered pairs does <u>not</u> represent a function?

A. (-5, 0), (-3, 1), (2, 1)

B. (5, 0), (1, 3), (1, 5)

SHOW YOUR WORK

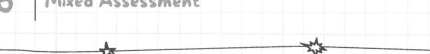

35. Which of the following represents a linear function? Explain your reasoning.

x	y
0	1
0	2
0	3
0	4

A.

x	y
1	1
2	2
3	3
4	4

B.

SHOW YOUR WORK

36. Which of the following represents a function? Explain your reasoning.

x	y
-1	0
0	3.5
1	0

A.

x	y
-1	2
0	5
-1	8

B.

SHOW YOUR WORK

37. (1, 3) and (3, 9) are points on the graph of a linear function. Which point also lies on the graph of this function?

A. (5, 12)

SHOW YOUR WORK

B. (2, 6)

38. (10, 1) and (20, 2) are points on the graph of a linear function. Which point also lies on the graph of this function?

A. (30, 3)

B. (30, 4)

SHOW YOUR WORK

Use the representations below to answer questions 29-30.

Representation A

x	y
-5	1
-3	2
-1	3

Representation B

$$2y = 20x + 10$$

39. Which representation has a greater rate of change?

SHOW YOUR WORK

40. Which representation has a greater y-intercept?

SHOW YOUR WORK

41. Write an equation that models the linear relationship in the table.

x	0	2
y	-4	0

SHOW YOUR WORK

42. Write an equation that models the linear relationship in the table.

x	4	8
y	0	1

SHOW YOUR WORK

43. Write an equation that models the linear relationship in the graph.

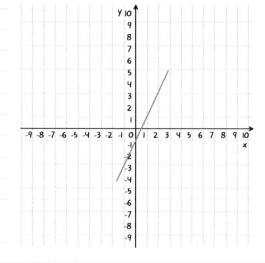

SHOW YOUR WORK

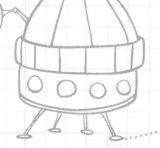

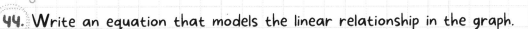

44. Write an equation that models the linear relationship in the graph.

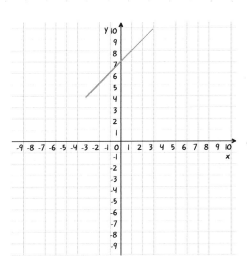

SHOW YOUR WORK

45. Write an equation for the line that has a rate of change of 4 and passes through the point (0, 2).

SHOW YOUR WORK

46. Write an equation for the line that has a rate of change of $\frac{1}{5}$ and passes through the point (-5, -3).

SHOW YOUR WORK

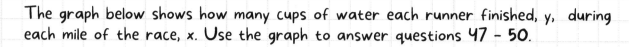

The graph below shows how many cups of water each runner finished, y, during each mile of the race, x. Use the graph to answer questions 47 – 50.

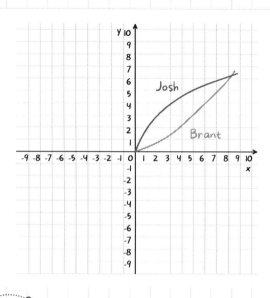

SHOW YOUR WORK

47. .... drank more during the first **5** miles of the race?

A. Brant

B. Josh

C. They drank the same amount

SHOW YOUR WORK

48. At what mile had Brant and Josh had the same amount of water?

A. Mile 2

B. Mile 5

C. Mile 8

SHOW YOUR WORK

49. Josh had drunk .... ounce(s) more than Brant by Mile **5**.

A. 1

B. 2

C. 3

SHOW YOUR WORK

50. At what point in the race does Brant start drinking more than Josh?

A. After Mile **2**

B. After Mile **6**

C. After Mile **8**

SHOW YOUR WORK

51. What single transformation was applied to rectangle A to get rectangle B?

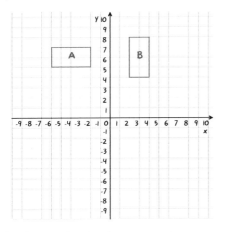

A. Rotation

B. Reflection

C. Translation

SHOW YOUR WORK

52. What single transformation was applied to rectangle A to get rectangle B?

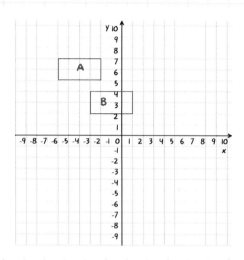

A. Rotation

B. Reflection

C. Translation

SHOW YOUR WORK

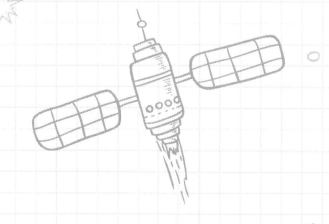

53. What single transformation was applied to triangle A to get triangle B?

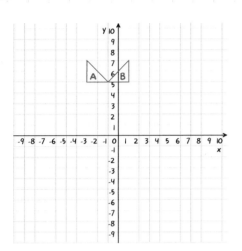

A. Rotation

B. Reflection

C. Translation

SHOW YOUR WORK

54. Plot the image of Point A under a reflection across line v.

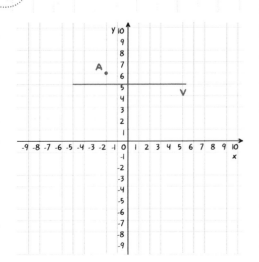

SHOW YOUR WORK

55. Draw the line of reflection for Triangle A onto Triangle B.

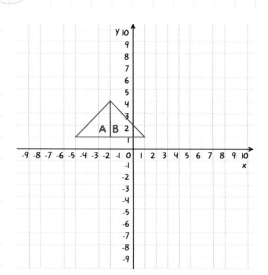

SHOW YOUR WORK

56. Triangle B is the image of Triangle A under a rotation around the origin. Determine the angle of rotation.

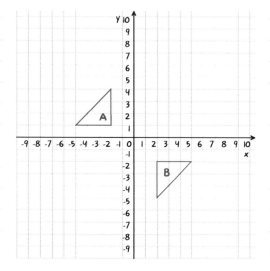

SHOW YOUR WORK

57. Point A' (2, 4) represents Point A (6, -1) under a translation. Point A' represents a translation by .... units to the .... and .... units ....

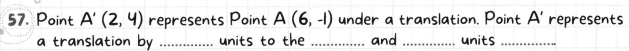

SHOW YOUR WORK

Rectangle ABCD is rotated **90°** clockwise around the origin to form rectangle WXYZ. Use the rectangles to answer questions **58 - 59**.

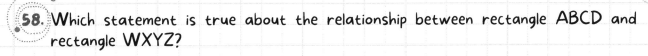

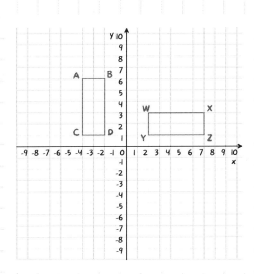

SHOW YOUR WORK

58. Which statement is true about the relationship between rectangle ABCD and rectangle WXYZ?

A. $\overline{AB} \cong \overline{WX}$

B. $\overline{AB} \cong \overline{XZ}$

C. $\overline{AB} \cong \overline{ZY}$

D. $\overline{AB} \cong \overline{YW}$

SHOW YOUR WORK

59. Which statement is true about the relationship between rectangle ABCD and rectangle WXYZ?

A. $\overline{CA} \cong \overline{XW}$

B. $\overline{CA} \cong \overline{ZY}$

C. $\overline{CA} \cong \overline{WX}$

D. $\overline{CA} \cong \overline{YZ}$

SHOW YOUR WORK

60. Plot the image of point A under dilation about the origin with a scale of **2**.

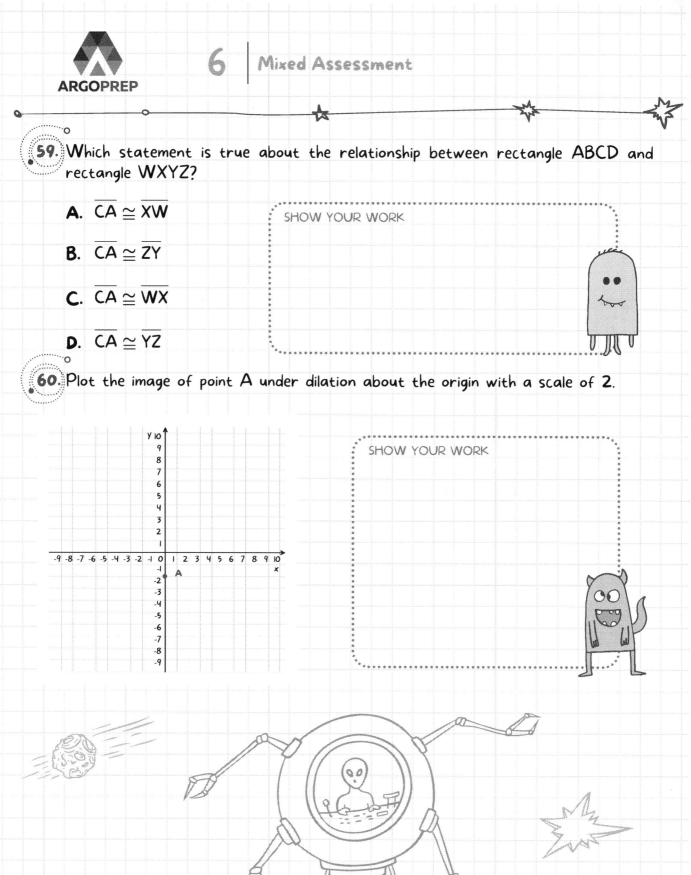

SHOW YOUR WORK

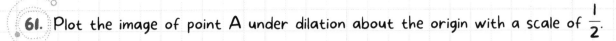

61. Plot the image of point A under dilation about the origin with a scale of $\frac{1}{2}$.

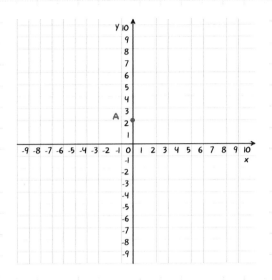

SHOW YOUR WORK

62. Use the coordinate plane to determine if the triangles are similar.

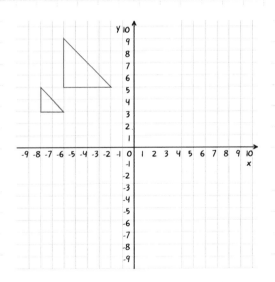

SHOW YOUR WORK

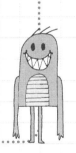

63. Explain why the figures are/aren't similar.

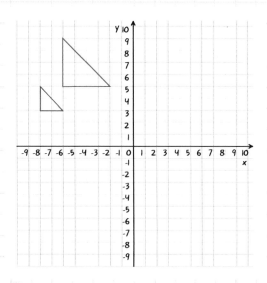

SHOW YOUR WORK

64. Find the volume of the cone.

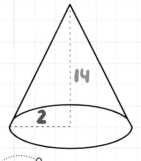

SHOW YOUR WORK

65. Find the volume of the sphere

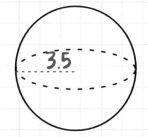

SHOW YOUR WORK

66. Find the volume of the cylinder

12

4

SHOW YOUR WORK

67. Fill in the missing values. ....^{2} + ...^{2} = c^2

16

100

SHOW YOUR WORK

68. Fill in the missing values. .... + ... = c^2

12

4

SHOW YOUR WORK

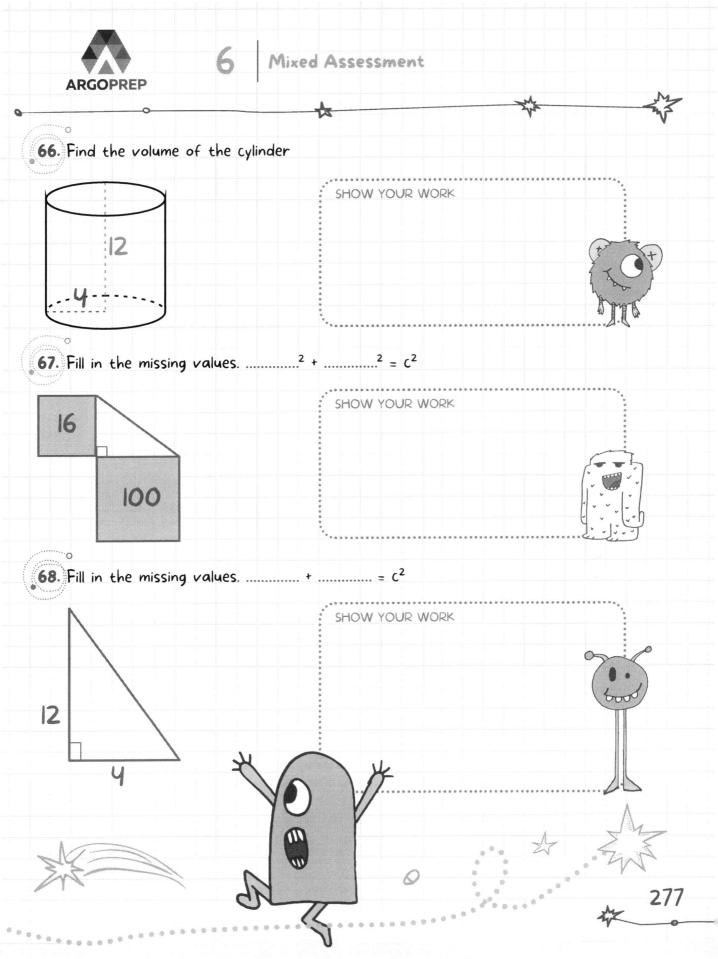

69. Solve for side a.

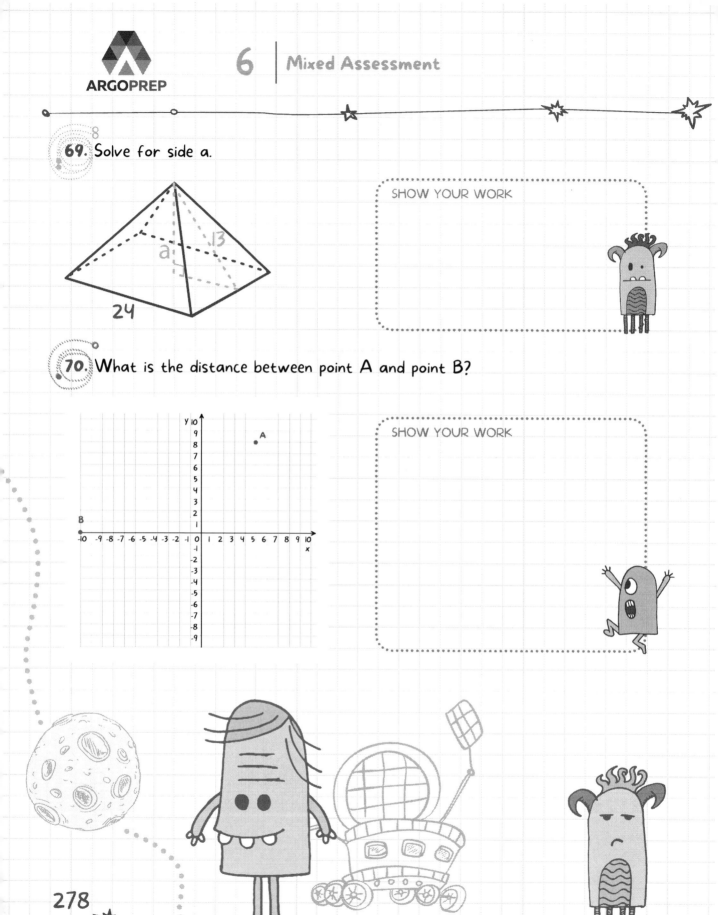

13

a

24

SHOW YOUR WORK

70. What is the distance between point A and point B?

SHOW YOUR WORK

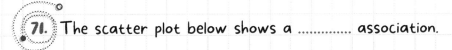

71. The scatter plot below shows a .... association.

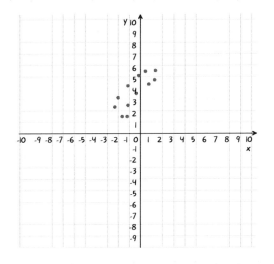

SHOW YOUR WORK

A. Negative

B. Positive

72. The scatter plot below shows a .... association.

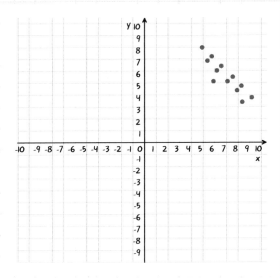

SHOW YOUR WORK

A. Negative

B. Positive

73. The scatter plot below shows a .... association.

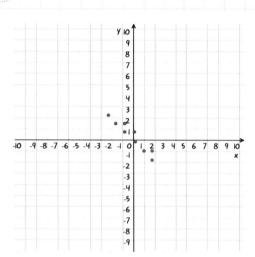

SHOW YOUR WORK

A. Linear

B. Nonlinear

74. The scatter plot below shows a .... association.

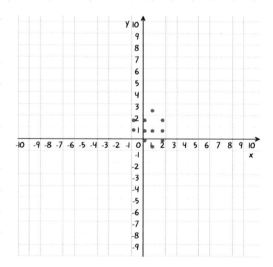

SHOW YOUR WORK

A. Linear

B. Nonlinear

75. The scatter plot below has a/an ....?

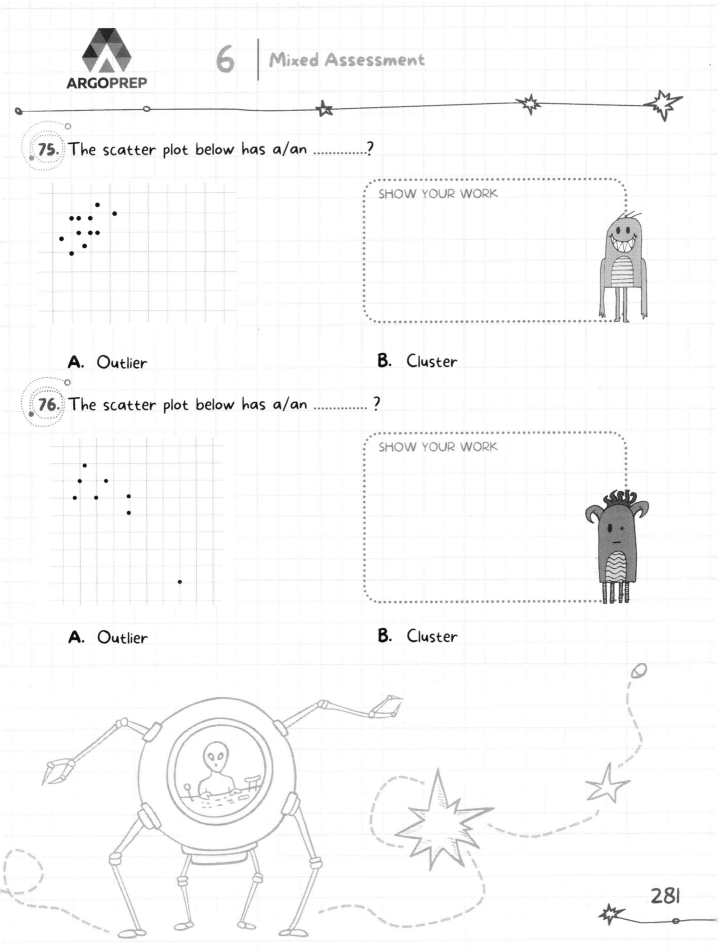

SHOW YOUR WORK

A. Outlier

B. Cluster

76. The scatter plot below has a/an .... ?

SHOW YOUR WORK

A. Outlier

B. Cluster

The table below shows the relationship between school absences and student grade level. Use the scatter plot below to answer questions 77 - 80.

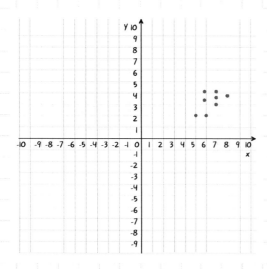

77. What is the association between the two variables?

SHOW YOUR WORK

78. Draw the line of best fit for the scatter plot.

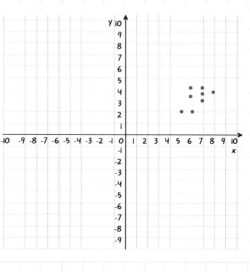

79. What prediction could be made based on the scatter plot?

A. There is a cluster

B. There is an outlier

C. None of the above

SHOW YOUR WORK

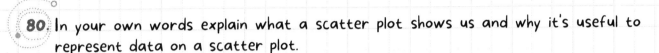

80 In your own words explain what a scatter plot shows us and why it's useful to represent data on a scatter plot.

WRITE YOUR RESPONSE HERE

NOTES

The graph below shows the relationship between gallons of gas and miles driven during different trainings for an upcoming race. The line of best fit is given. Use the graph to answer questions 81 – 85.

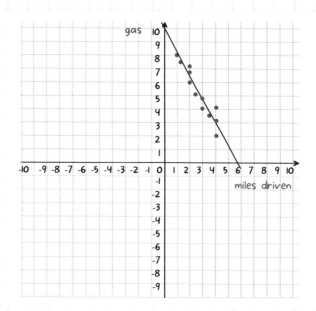

81. What is the association between the two variables?

SHOW YOUR WORK

82. What is the y-intercept of the best fitting line?

SHOW YOUR WORK

83. What is the slope of the best fitting line?

> SHOW YOUR WORK

84. Write a linear equation to represent the model.

> SHOW YOUR WORK

85. Which of the following statements is a valid prediction?

A. The driver will use half of his gas before mile **2**

B. The driver will use half of his gas before mile **4**

C. None of the above

> SHOW YOUR WORK

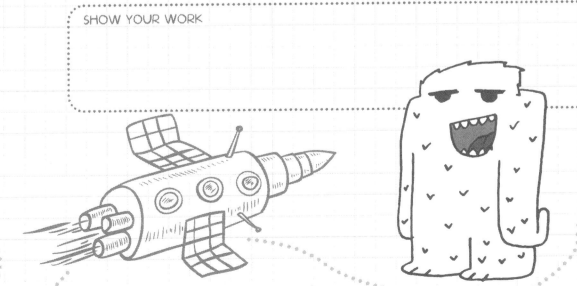

86. Which of the following statements is a valid prediction?

A. The driver will need to refuel between mile **5** and **6**

B. The driver will need to refuel between mile **8** and **9**

C. None of the above

SHOW YOUR WORK

Use the table below to answer questions **87 – 93**.

Preference	Males	Females
Swimming	22	24
Basketball	31	23

87. How many people were surveyed?

SHOW YOUR WORK

88. How many males were surveyed?

SHOW YOUR WORK

89. How many females were surveyed?

SHOW YOUR WORK

90. What percent of males preferred swimming? Round to the nearest tenth.

SHOW YOUR WORK

91. What percent of males preferred basketball?

SHOW YOUR WORK

92. What percent of females preferred basketball?

SHOW YOUR WORK

93. What percent of females preferred swimming?

SHOW YOUR WORK

Use the table below to answer questions 94 – 100.

Preference	Parents	Children
Spaghetti Dinner	15	7
Hamburger Dinner	5	13

94. How many people were surveyed?

SHOW YOUR WORK

95. How many children were surveyed?

SHOW YOUR WORK

96. How many parents were surveyed?

SHOW YOUR WORK

97. How many more parents preferred spaghetti dinner than children?

SHOW YOUR WORK

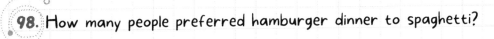

98. How many people preferred hamburger dinner to spaghetti?

SHOW YOUR WORK

99. How many people preferred spaghetti to hamburger dinner?

SHOW YOUR WORK

100. What percent of children preferred hamburger dinner?

SHOW YOUR WORK

NOTES

ANSWER SHEET

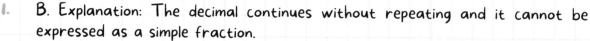

Chapter 1

1.1.A. Irrational Numbers

1. B. Explanation: The decimal continues without repeating and it cannot be expressed as a simple fraction.

2. A. Explanation: The number can be expressed as a fraction of two integers. We can write 0.125 in fraction form as $\frac{1}{8}$.

3. A. Explanation: The number can be expressed as $\frac{1}{3}$. The decimal is infinite but it repeats.

4. B. Explanation: The decimal continues without repeating and it cannot be expressed as a simple fraction.

5. A. Explanation: The number can be expressed as $1\frac{1}{2}$. It also ends after one digit.

6. A. Explanation: The square root of 4 is 2, which is rational.

7. A. Explanation: The number is a simple fraction.

8. B. Explanation: The decimal continues without repeating and it cannot be expressed as a simple fraction.

9. A. Explanation: The number can be expressed as $-\frac{3}{1}$.

10. B. Explanation: The decimal continues without repeating and it cannot be expressed as a simple fraction.

11. A. Explanation: The number is a simple fraction.

12. B. Explanation: The decimal continues without repeating and it cannot be expressed as a simple fraction

13. A. Explanation: The number can be expressed as $-1\frac{13}{25}$.

14. A. Explanation: The number can be expressed as $\frac{51234}{1}$

15. A. Explanation: The number can be expressed as $\frac{0}{1}$

16. A, C. Explanation: The number can be expressed as $\frac{-2}{1}$. Whole numbers cannot be negative.

17. B. Explanation: The number cannot be expressed as two fractional intergers.

18. A. Explanation: The number is expressed as a fraction of two integers.
19. A, C. Explanation: The number can be expressed as $\frac{-6}{1}$. Whole numbers cannot be negative.
20. A, C, D. Explanation: The number can be expressed as $\frac{0}{1}$.

1.1.B Approximating Irrational Numbers

1.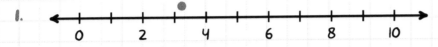

2.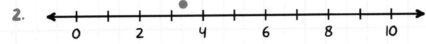

3.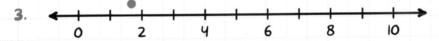

4.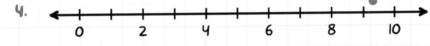

5.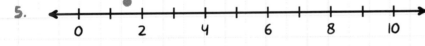

6.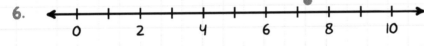

7. -4, 4, $\sqrt{24}$, 5. Explanation: $\sqrt{24}$ is between 4.5 and 5.

8. $\frac{5}{2}$, 3, π, 4. Explanation: π is between 3 and 4. $\frac{5}{2}$ is 2.5.

9. 3, $\sqrt{10}$, 4. Explanation: $\sqrt{10}$ is between 3.1 and 3.2.

10. 3, $\sqrt{14}$, 4, 5. Explanation: $\sqrt{14}$ is between 3.7 and 3.8.

11. 1, 3, 6, 2π. Explanation: 2 times 3.14... will be somewhere after 6 and before 6.3.

12. 1, $\frac{1}{2}\pi$, 2, 3 . Explanation: π times $\frac{1}{2}$ is 1.5.

13. Answers may vary. Explanation: π - 2 is between 1.1 and 1.2.

14. Answers may vary. Explanation: $\sqrt{83}$ is between 9.1 and 9.2.
15. Answers may vary. Explanation: 12π is between 37 and 38.
16. Answers may vary. Explanation: $\sqrt{75}$ is between 8.5 and 9.
17. Answers may vary. Explanation: $\sqrt{5}$ is between 2 and 3.
18. 1.7. Explanation: $1.7^3 = 4.9$ and $1.8^3 = 5.832$
19. 2.4. Explanation: $2.4^2 = 5.76$
20. 19. Explanation: $3.14... \times 2 = 6.2 \times 3 = 18.8$. Round to nearest number -> 19

1.2 Chapter Test

1. B. Explanation: The decimal continues without repeating and it cannot be expressed as a simple fraction.
2. A. Explanation: The number can be expressed as 3 over 4.
3. B. Explanation: The decimal continues without repeating and it cannot be expressed as a simple fraction.
4. A. Explanation: The number can be expressed as -2 over 1.
5. A. Explanation: The number can be expressed as 3 over 1.
6. A. Explanation: Even though the decimal continues, it repeats. The number can be expressed as 4 over 9.
7. B. Explanation: The decimal continues without repeating and it cannot be expressed as a simple fraction.
8. A. Explanation: The number is expressed as a fraction of two integers.
9. B. Explanation: The decimal continues without repeating and it cannot be expressed as a simple fraction.
10. A. Explanation: The number can be expressed as 9 over 1.

11.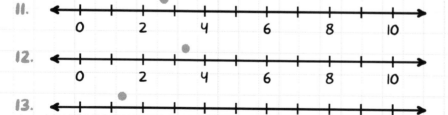

12.

13.

14. 18

15. 1

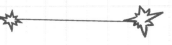

16. 12

17. 9, 10, $\sqrt{112}$, 11. Explanation: 10^2 is 100 and 11^2 is 121.

18. 4, $\sqrt{24}$, 5. Explanation: 5^2 is 25 and 4^2 is 16.

19. $\sqrt{8}$, 3, 4. Explanation: 3^3 is 9 and 4^2 is 16.

20. 5, $\sqrt{34}$, 6. Explanation: 5^2 is 25 and 6^2 is 36.

Chapter 2

2.1.A Properties of Integer Exponents

1. 17. Explanation: $(-2)^4 = 16 + 1 = 17$

2. $\dfrac{1}{25}$. Explanation: $\dfrac{1}{5} \times \dfrac{1}{5} = \dfrac{1}{25}$

3. 144. Explanation: $(3^2) = 9.\ (4^2) = 16.\ 9 \times 16 = 144$

4. 25. Explanation: $5^{6-4} = 5^2$

5. -36. Explanation: $-(6 \times 6) = -36$

6. 256. Explanation: $4^{3+1=4} = 4^4 = 256$

7. 162. Explanation: $3^4 = 81.\ (-3)^4 = 81.\ 81 + 81 = 162$

8. $\dfrac{1}{144}$. Explanation: $\dfrac{1}{12} \times \dfrac{1}{12} = \dfrac{1}{144}$

9. $\dfrac{1}{8}$. Explanation: $8^{2-3\ =\ -1} = 8^{-1} = \dfrac{1}{8}$

10. 4. Explanation: $\dfrac{2}{1} \times \dfrac{2}{1} = \dfrac{4}{1}$

11. 81. Explanation: $(-3) \times (-3) \times (-3) \times (-3) = 81$

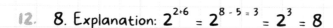

12. 8. Explanation: $2^{2+6} = 2^{8-5=3} = 2^3 = 8$

13. 1. Explanation: $25^{3+(-3)=0} = 1$

14. 1. Explanation: Any number to the power of 0 is 1.

15. -125. Explanation: $(-5) \times (-5) \times (-5) = -125$

2.1.B Square Roots

1.   8. Explanation: $8 \times 8 = 64$
2.   6. Explanation: $6 \times 6 = 36$
3.   11. Explanation: $11 \times 11 = 121$
4.   3. Explanation: $3 \times 3 = 9$
5.   5. Explanation: $5 \times 5 = 25$
6.   4. Explanation: $4 \times 4 \times 4 = 64$
7.   7. Explanation: $7 \times 7 \times 7 = 343$
8.   5. Explanation: $5 \times 5 \times 5 = 125$
9.   3. Explanation: $3 \times 3 \times 3 = 27$
10. 10. Explanation: $10 \times 10 \times 10 = 1000$
11. $x = 81$. Explanation: $9 \times 9 = 81$
12. $x = 49$. Explanation: $7 \times 7 = 49$
13. $x = 100$. Explanation: $10 \times 10 = 100$
14. $x = 729$. Explanation: $9 \times 9 \times 9 = 729$
15. 1728. Explanation: $12 \times 12 \times 12 = 1728$

2.1.C Powers of Ten

1.   40,000,000. Explanation: Move the decimal 7 spaces to the right.
2.   .05. Explanation: Move the decimal 2 spaces to the left.
3.   100,000,000,000. Explanation: Move the decimal 10 spaces to the left.
4. $x = -2$. Explanation: The decimal is two places to the *left*.
5. $x = 3$. Explanation: The decimal is three spaces to the *right*.
6.   1. Explanation: The decimal is one space to the *right*.

7. D. Explanation: First divide the integers, $2 \div 1 = 2$. Then calculate the power of ten, $10^{7-1=6}$. Finally, combine the answers to get $2 \times 10^6 = 2,000,000$.

8. C. Explanation: First divide the integers, $9 \div 3 = 3$. Then calculate the power of ten, $10^{4-2=2}$. Finally, combine the answers to get $3 \times 10^2 = 300$.

9. B. Explanation: First divide the integers, $6 \div 2 = 3$. Then calculate the power of ten, $10^{4-3=1}$. Finally, combine the answers to get $3 \times 10^1 = 30$.

10. A. Explanation: First, round 3,210 to 3,000, which is 3×1000 (3 zeros). Then rewrite as scientific notation, which is 3×10^3.

11. A. Explanation: Rewrite .1 in scientific notation. The decimal is one space to the left of the 1, which can be written as 1×10^{-1}.

12. D. Explanation: $(3 \times 10^3) \div (1 \times 10^{-1}) = 3 \times 10^{3-(-1)} = 3 \times 10^4$

13. B. Explanation: $2 \times 10^4 = 20,000$

14. B. Explanation: $8 \times 10^6 = 8,000,000$

15. C. Explanation: First divide the integers $8 \div 2 = 4$. Then, subtract the exponents $10^{6-4=2}$. $4 \times 10^2 = 400$

2.1.D Performing Operations with Scientific Notation

1. 3.37×10^4. Explanation: $1,700 + 32,000 = 33,700$

2. 3.09×10^{-1}. Explanation: $.263 + .046 = .309$

3. 7.03×10^6. Explanation: $6,800,000 + 230,000 = 7,030,000$

4. 4.84×10^{-1}. Explanation: $.054 + .43 = .484$

5. 4.2×10^2. Explanation: $520 - 100 = 420$

6. 6.15×10^4. Explanation: $63000 - 1500 = 61,500$

7. 1.98×10^4. Explanation: $27,000 - 7200 = 19,800$

8. 3.74×10^6. Explanation: $1.1 \times 3.4 = 3.74 \times 10^{2+4=6}$

9. 4.08×10^1. Explanation: Rewrite as $(1.2 \times 10^3) \times (3.4 \times 10^{-2}) = 1.2 \times 3.4 = 4.08 \times 10^{3+(-2)}$

10. 2.604×10^8. Explanation: $6.2 \times 4.2 = 26.04 \times 10^{5+2=7} \rightarrow 2.604 \times 10^8$

11. 3.0×10^2. Explanation: $36000 \div 120 = 300$

12. 1.2×10^1. Explanation: $2.4 \div 2.0 = 1.2 \times 10^{3-2=1}$

13. 3.0×10^{-2}. Explanation: $2.7 \div 9.0 = .3 \times 10^{-3--2=-1}$

14. 9.25 pounds. Explanation: $7.4 \times 1.25 = 9.25 \times 10^{2+(-2)=0}$

15. 3. Explanation: Rewrite as $3.6 \times 10^5 \div 1.2 \times 10^5 = 3.6 \div 1.2 = 3$

2.2A   Graphing Linear Equations

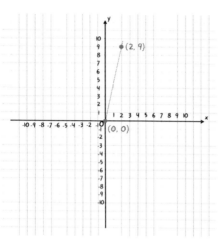

1.

The slope is $\dfrac{9}{2}$

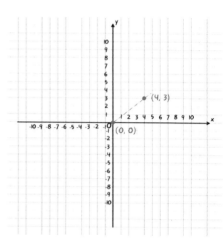

3.

The slope is $\dfrac{3}{4}$

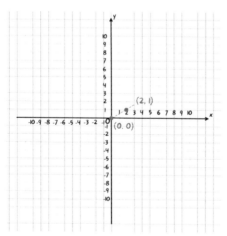

2.

The slope is $\dfrac{1}{2}$

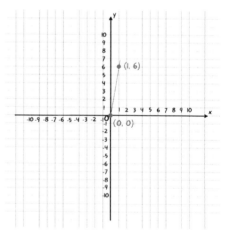

4.

The slope is $\dfrac{6}{1}$

ARGOPREP

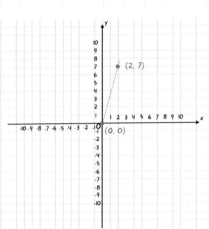

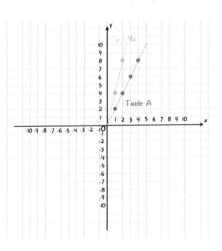

5.

The slope is $\dfrac{7}{2}$

6. **2.** Explanation: $\dfrac{(4-2)}{(2-1)} = 2$

7. Use the x-coordinates and y-coordinates to graph each point

8. Insert the value for x to determine y

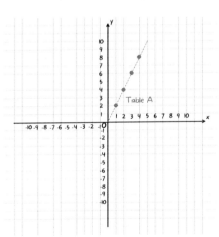

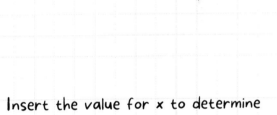

9. **B.** Explanation: The slope of the line representing the equation is greater than the slope of the line representing the table.

10. B. Explanation: The steeper the slope, the greater the unit rate of change.

11. The equation. Explanation: The slope of the equation is $\frac{5}{1}$ and the slope of the graph is $\frac{5}{2}$.

12. The equation. Explanation: $\frac{3}{2}$ is greater than $\frac{1}{2}$

13. The equation. Explanation $3.2 > 2/7$

14. The equation. Explanation: $\frac{7}{5}$ is greater than $\frac{6}{5}$

15. Answers may vary. Explanation: The unit rate of change should be less than $\frac{3}{2}$.

2.2.B   Determining Y-Intercepts and Explaining Slope

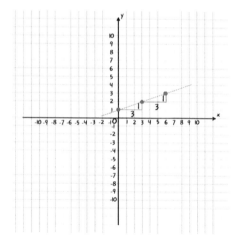

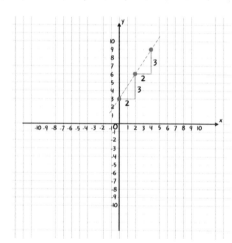

1.

Slope $= \frac{1}{3}$

2.

Slope $= \frac{3}{2}$

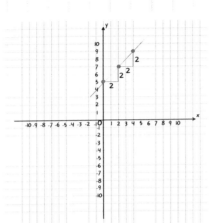

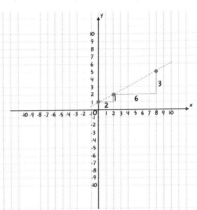

3.

Slope = 1
Each triangle has a height of **2** and a base of **2**, which can be written as $\frac{2}{2}$. Simplify $\frac{2}{2}$ to get 1.

4.

Slope = $\frac{1}{2}$
The first triangle has a height of **1** and a base of **2** for a slope of $\frac{1}{2}$. The second triangle has a height of **3** and a base of **6** for a slope of $\frac{3}{6}$, which can be simplified to $\frac{1}{2}$.

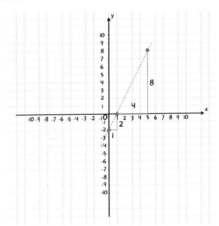

5.

Slope = **2**
The first triangle has a height of **2** and a base of **1** for a slope of **2**. The second triangle has a height of **8** and a base of **4** for a slope of $\frac{8}{4}$, which can be simplified to **2**.

6. Slope = $\frac{2}{5}$. Explanation: Rewrite the equation in slope-intercept form $y = \frac{2}{5}x$

7. Slope = $\frac{1}{2}$. Explanation: Rewrite the equation in slope-intercept form $y = \frac{1}{2}x + 3$

8. Slope = 2. Explanation: Rewrite the equation in slope-intercept form $y = 2x - 4$

9. Slope = 2. Explanation: Rewrite the equation in slope-intercept form $y = 2x + 1$

10. Slope = $\frac{5}{3}$. Explanation: Rewrite the equation in slope-intercept form $y = \frac{5}{3}x - \frac{1}{3}$

11. y-intercept = 2. Explanation: Plug 0 in for x to determine the y-intercept. $y = 3(0) + 2$

12. y-intercept = -2. Explanation: Plug 0 in for x to determine the y-intercept. $y = 4.5(0) - 2$

13. y-intercept = -4. Explanation: Rewrite the equation in slope-intercept form. Then, plug 0 in for x to determine the y-intercept. $y = 2(0) - 4$

14. y-intercept = 2. Explanation: Rewrite the equation in slope-intercept form. Then, plug 0 in for x to determine the y-intercept. $y = 5(0) + 2$

15. y-intercept = 0. Explanation: Plug 0 in for x to determine the y-intercept. $y = 3.5(0)$

2.3.A Solving Linear Equations

1. A. Explanation: Isolate the variable to determine that $x = \frac{5}{4}$.

2. C. Explanation: Simplify both sides of the equation to determine that they are equal.

3. B. Explanation: Simplify both sides of the equation to determine that the variables cancel each other out.

4. B. Explanation: Simplify both sides of the equation to determine that the variables cancel each other out.

5. A. Explanation: Isolate the variable to determine that $x = -5$.

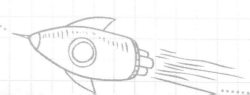

6. B. Explanation: Simplify both sides of the equation to determine that the variables cancel each other out.

7. C. Explanation: Simplify both sides of the equation to determine that they are equal.

8. $y = 1$. Explanation: First calculate $4 = 12y - 8y$. Then calculate $4 = 4y$. So, $y = 1$.

9. $w = 2$. Explanation: First calculate $-1 + 2w = 11 - 4w$. - Then calculate $12 = -6w$. So, $2 = w$.

10. $t = \dfrac{10}{7}$. Explanation: Simplify both sides and isolate the variable to determine that $t = \dfrac{10}{7}$.

11. $v = -1$. Explanation: Simplify both sides and isolate the variable to determine that $v = -1$.

12. $x = 0$. Explanation: Simplify both sides and isolate the variable to determine that $x = 0$.

13. $w = -2$. Explanation: Simplify both sides and isolate the variable to determine that $w = -2$.

14. $m = -\dfrac{1}{2}$. Explanation: Simplify both sides and isolate the variable to determine that $m = -\dfrac{1}{2}$.

15. 1. Explanation: Simplify both sides and isolate the variable to determine that $s = 1$.

2.3.B Solving Pairs of Linear Equations

1.

Time (Months)	1	2	3	4
Lawn A (inches)	3	4	5	6
Lawn B (inches)	3	5	7	9

2. $y = 1x + 2$. Explanation: The slope is 1, the y-intercept is 2

3. $y = 2x + 1$. Explanation: The slope is 2, the y-intercept is 1

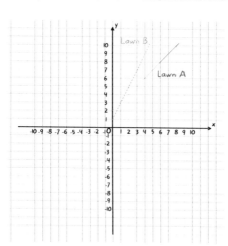

4.

5. (1, 3). Explanation: Find the point on the graph where the lines cross.

6. Answers may vary. Explanation: The grass in both lawns will be **3** inches tall after 1 month.

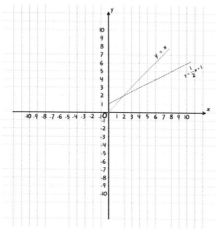

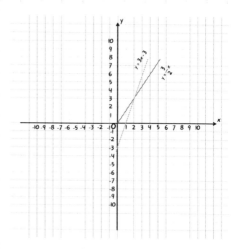

7.

8.

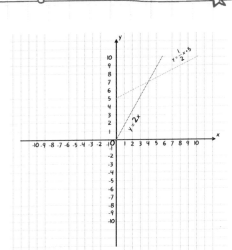

9.

10. (3, 0). Explanation: $0 = \frac{2}{3}(3) - 2$ and $0 = \frac{4}{3}(3) - 4$

11. (4, 6). Explanation: $6 = \frac{3}{2}(4)$ and $6 = 3(4)$

12. (-2, -6). Explanation: $-6 = \frac{3}{2}(-2) - 3$ and $-6 = 2(-2) - 2$

13. (-8, -30). Explanation: $30 = 3.5(-8) - 2$ and $30 = 3(-8) - 6$

14. Dan's hair will be the same length as Sally's after one year.

Time (years)	0	1	2
Dan's Hair (inches)	3	8	13
Sally's Hair (inches)	5	8	11

15. $y = 5x + 3$ and $y = 3x + 5$. Explanation: Use the slope formula to solve for m. Use the y-intercept to solve for b.

2.4 Chapter Test

1. 2. Explanation: 2 x 2 x 2 = 8
2. 15. Explanation: 15 x 15 = 225
3. 8. Explanation: 8 x 8 = 64
4. 3. Explanation: 3 x 3 x 3 = 27
5. 216. Explanation: 6 x 6 x 6 = 216
6. 1,000. Explanation: 10 x 10 x 10 = 1,000
7. B. Explanation: $1.6 \times 10^2 = 160$
8. A. Explanation: $6.6 \times 10^5 = 660,000$
9. 4.125×10^3.

    $\dfrac{6.6 \times 10^5}{1.6 \times 10^2}$

10. 3.35×10^4. Explanation: 3×10^4 is 30,000. Then add 3,500.
11. 4.24×10^{-2}. Explanation: 2.4×10^{-3} is .0024. Then add .04.
12. 7.5×10^1. Explanation: 2.5×10^2 is 250. Then calculate 325 - 250.
13. 8×10^3. Explanation: 1.5×10^2 is 150. Then calculate 8,150 - 150.

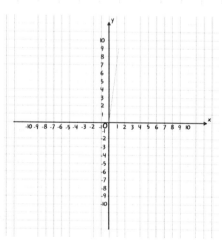

14.

15. The unit rate of change is 8. Calculate slope to determine the unit rate of change. $\dfrac{(8 - 0)}{(1 - 0)} = 8$

16. The slope in the graph is less than the slope in the equation. The slope is not as steep.

17. B. Explanation: Simplify both sides and isolate *x* to determine that the variables cancel out.

18. C. Explanation: Simplify both sides to determine that the equations are equal

19. 2 weeks

Time (weeks)	0	1	2
Lauren's plant (inches)	1	4	7
Hannah's plant (inches)	3	5	7

20. y = **3**x + **1** and y = **2**x + **3**. Explanation: Use the slope formula to slove for *m*. Use the y-intercept to solve for *b*.

Chapter 3: Functions

3.1.A Intro to Functions

1. Yes. Explanation: Each input (*x*-value) only has one output (*y*-value).
2. Yes. Explanation: Each input (*x*-value) only has one output (*y*-value).
3. No. Explanation: Some inputs (*x*-values) have more than one output (*y*-values).
4. No. Explanation: Some inputs (*x*-values) have more than one output (*y*-values).
5. Yes. Explanation: Each input (*x*-value) only has one output (*y*-value).
6. Yes. Explanation: Each input (*x*-value) only has one output (*y*-value).
7. No. Explanation: Some inputs (*x*-values) have more than one output (*y*-values).
8. Yes. Explanation: Each input (*x*-value) only has one output (*y*-value).
9. Yes. Explanation: Each input (*x*-value) only has one output (*y*-value).
10. No. Explanation: Some inputs (*x*-values) have more than one output (*y*-values).
11. B. Explanation: *x* = 3 has more than one output (*y*-values).
12. B. Explanation: *x* = 1 has more than one output (*y*-values).
13. A. Explanation: *x* = 0 has more than one output (*y*-values).
14. B. Explanation: *x* = 3 has more than one output (*y*-values).
15. A. Explanation: *x* = 2 has more than one output (*y*-values).
16. Yes. Explanation: Each input (color) has only one output (number of student votes) associated with it.

17. Yes. Explanation: Each input (hair style) has only one output (meal ordered) associated with it.

18. No. Explanation: The input for age 10 has more than one output (**5** miles ran and **2** miles ran).

19. No. Explanation: The input for hazel and blue eyes are repeated with different values.

20. Yes. Explanation: Each input (city) has only one output (amount of rainfall) associated with it.

3.1.B Comparing Functions

1. $\frac{1}{2}$. Explanation: Slope $= \frac{y_2 - y_1}{x_2 - x_1}$.

2. 2. Explanation: The equation is written in slope-intercept form, $y = mx + b$, where m = slope.

3. Representation B. Explanation: The unit rate of change is equal to slope.

4. 0. Explanation: The y-intercept is where the line crosses the y-axis.

5. 3. Explanation: The equation is written in slope-intercept form, $y = mx + b$, where b = y-intercept.

6. Representation B. Explanation: **3 > 0**.

7. 3. Explanation: Slope $= \frac{y_2 - y_1}{x_2 - x_1}$.

8. 1. Explanation: Each point is up one unit and over one unit $\left(\frac{1}{1}\right)$ from the previous point.

9. Representation A. Explanation: The unit rate of change is equal to slope. **3 > 1**

10. 10. Explanation: The y-intercept is where x = **0**.

11. 2. Explanation: The y-intercept is where the line crosses the y-axis.

12. Representation A. Explanation: **10 > 2**.

13. $y = 2x + \frac{5}{2}$. Explanation: Isolate the y by dividing both sides by **2**.

14. $-\frac{1}{2}$. Explanation: Each point is separate by 1 unit down and **2** units over.

15. Representation A. Explanation: The unit rate of change is equal to slope.

16. Representation A. Explanation: A has a y-intercept of **2.5**. B has a y-intercept of -**2**.

17. $y = 3x - 1$. Explanation: Isolate the y by dividing both sides by 3.

18. Jinger. Explanation: The unit rate of change is equal to slope. The slope of A is $\frac{3}{4}$. The slope of B is 3.

19. Heather. Explanation: Heather sold 3 cookies on day one. Jinger sold 2 cookies on day one ($y = 3(1) - 1$).

20. Jinger. Explanation: Jinger sold 14 cookies on day 5 ($y = 3(5) - 1$). Heather sold 6.

3.1.C Nonlinear Functions

1. A. Explanation: B is nonlinear because it does not have a constant slope.

2. A. Explanation: B is nonlinear because it does not have a constant slope.

3. A. Explanation: B is nonlinear because it does not have a constant slope.

4. B.

5. A. Explanation: B is nonlinear because it does not have a constant slope. $(-2, 4)$ and $(1,4)$ are both points on the graph.

6. B. Explanation: A is nonlinear because it does not have a constant slope. $(-1, 10)$ and $(-1, 2)$ are both points on the graph.

7. No. Explanation: The line is not a function.

8. No. Explanation: The graph is curved.

9. Yes. Explanation: The line has a constant slope.

10. Yes. Explanation: The line has a constant slope.

11. B. Explanation: The slope is 1.

12. A. Explanation: The slope is 1.

13. Answers may vary. The slope $\frac{4}{3}$. Explanation: All points should show a constant slope of $\frac{4}{3}$.

14. Answers may vary. The slope is $\frac{1}{2}$. Explanation: All points should show a constant slope of $\frac{1}{2}$.

15. Answers may vary. The slope is $\frac{1}{5}$. Explanation: All points should show a constant slope of 5.

3.2.A Constructing Functions

1. $y = 2x - 3$. Explanation: $m = \dfrac{5-1}{4-2}$. Plug values in for y and x to isolate b.

2. $y = \dfrac{1}{3}x + 3$. Explanation: $m = \dfrac{6-3}{5-4}$. Plug values in for y and x to isolate b.

3. $y = -\dfrac{1}{6}x + 6$. Explanation: $m = \dfrac{5-7}{6--6} = -\dfrac{2}{12}$. Plug values in for y and x to isolate b.

4. $y = x - 6$. Explanation: $m = \dfrac{-1-2}{5-8} = 1$. Plug values in for y and x to isolate b.

5. $y = \dfrac{1}{3}x + 5$. Explanation: $m = \dfrac{10-6}{15-3} = \dfrac{4}{12}$. Plug values in for y and x to isolate b.

6. $y = -\dfrac{1}{2}x + 5$. Explanation: Use triangles to determine slope $\dfrac{1}{2}$. Use x = 0 to determine y-intercept.

7. $y = -x + 6$. Explanation: Use triangles to determine slope 1. Use x = 0 to determine y-intercept.

8. $y = \dfrac{1}{2}x$. Explanation: Use triangles to determine slope $\dfrac{1}{3}$. Use x = 0 to determine y-intercept.

9. $y = \dfrac{4}{3}x - 2$ Explanation: Use triangles to determine slope 1. Use x = 0 to determine y-intercept.

10. $y = -x - 1$. Explanation: Use triangles to determine slope -1. Use x = 0 to determine y-intercept.

11. $y = 5x$. Explanation: Plug in x and y values to determine b. $5 = 5(1) + b$. The y-intercept is 0.

12. $y = \dfrac{2}{3}x + 3$. Explanation: Plug in x and y values to determine b. $5 = \dfrac{2}{3}(3) + b$. The y-intercept is 3.

13. $y = 3x + 5$. Explanation: Plug in x and y values to determine b. $2 = 3(-1) + b$.

14. The y-intercept is 1.
    $y = \dfrac{1}{3}x + 3$. Explanation: Plug in x and y values to determine b. $4 = \dfrac{1}{3}(3)+b$.

15. The y-intercept is 3.
    $y = 2x + 4$. Explanation: Plug in x and y values to determine b. $0 = 2(-2) + b$.
    The y-intercept is 4

16. $u = 2s + 10$. Explanation: s is the independent variable. 2 is the slope and 10 is the y-intercept.

17. $d = 10c + 10$. Explanation: c is the independent variable. 10 is the slope and 10 is the y-intercept.

18. $b = 3d + 5$. Explanation: d is the independent variable. 3 is the slope and 5 is the y-intercept.

19. $m = 65d + 100$. Explanation: d is the independent variable. 65 is the slope and 100 is the y-intercept.

20. $m = 25h + 50$. Explanation: h is the independent variable. 25 is the slope and 50 is the y-intercept.

3.2.B Analyzing Functional Relationships

1. B. Explanation: y increases with x.
2. B. Explanation: The slope does not stay the same.
3. B. Explanation: The slope does not stay the same.
4. 5. Explanation: The point is (8, 5).
5. 2. Explanation: Two is two times the size of one.
6. A. Explanation: The line representing Iris is higher than the line representing Sam.
7. B. Explanation: The lines intersect at Week 5.
8. A. Explanation: Sam's line increases while Iris takes a break from increases during weeks 3-5.
9. 1. Explanation: Sam swims 4 miles. Iris swims 3 miles. 4 - 3 = 1.
10. C. Explanation: The line does not increase or decrease.
11. A. Explanation: The line representing Dan's money is higher than the line representing Kathleen s money.

12. B. Explanation: Kathleen makes 8 dollars. Dan makes 4.
13. B. Explanation: The lines intersect at hour 5.
14. C. Explanation: Dan makes 3 dollars while Kathleen makes 1.
15. D. Explanation: Neither graph has a constant slope.

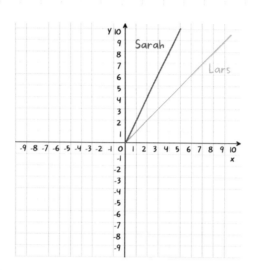

16 - 17.
18. C. Explanation: The slope is constant for both.
19. B. Explanation: Sara walks 10 miles. Lars walks 5.
20. A. Explanation: The line representing the number of miles Sarah walked is always above the line representing the number of miles Lars walked.

3.3 Chapter Test

1. Yes. Explanation: Each input (x-value) only has one output (y-value).
2. No. Explanation: Some inputs (x-value) have more than one output (y-value).
3. A. Explanation: A is not a function because some inputs (x-value) have more than one output (y-value).
4. B. Explanation: B is not a function because some inputs (x-value) have more than one output (y-value).
5. A. Explanation: B is not linear because the slope is not constant.
6. B. Explanation: A is not linear because the slope is not constant.

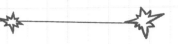

7. A. Explanation: The slope is $\frac{5}{2}$.

8. A. Explanation: The slope is $\frac{1}{6}$.

9. B. Explanation: A has a slope of 1. B has a slope of 3.

10. A. Explanation: Explanation: A has a y-intercept of 2. B has a y-intercept of 1.

11. $y = \frac{1}{2}x + 7$. Explanation: $m = \frac{10-8}{6-2} = \frac{2}{4}$. Plug values in for y and x to isolate b.

12. $y = -x + 5$. Explanation: $m = \frac{1-4}{4-1} = -1$. Plug values in for y and x to isolate b.

13. $y = 2x - 4$. Explanation: Use triangles to determine slope 2. Use $x = 0$ to determine y-intercept.

14. $y = -\frac{1}{2}x - 1$. Explanation: Use triangles to determine slope 2. Use $x = 0$ to determine y-intercept.

15. $y = \frac{1}{3}x + 1$. Explanation: Plug in x and y values to determine b. $2 = \frac{1}{3}(3) + b$. The y-intercept is 1.

16. $y = -2x + 17$. Explanation: Plug in x and y values to determine b. $7 = -2(5) + b$. The y-intercept is 17.

17. B. Explanation: The line representing Jim is higher than the line representing Pam for the first part of the graph.

18. B. Explanation: The lines intersect at Mile 4.

19. A. Explanation: Jim's line is at 3. Pam's line is at 2. $3 - 2 = 1$.

20. A. Explanation: Pam finishes her water at mile 5.

Chapter 4

4.1.A Experimenting with Rotations, Reflections and Translations

1. 180°. Explanation: The point is rotated 180 degrees around the origin.
2. 180°. Explanation: The point is rotated 180 degrees around the origin.
3. 270°. Explanation: The point is rotated 270 degrees around the origin.
4. 90°. Explanation: The point is rotated 90 degrees around the origin.
5. 180°. Explanation: The point is rotated 180 degrees around the origin.

6.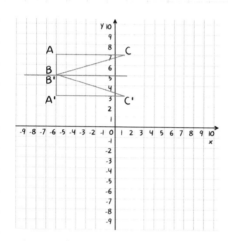

7.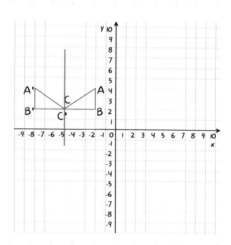

8. (-2, 5). Explanation: The point of reflection should appear at (-2, 5)
9. (6, 0). Explanation: The point of reflection should appear at (6, 0)
10. (-3, 4). Explanation: The point of reflection should appear at (-3, 2)
11. The point of reflection should appear at (-7, 7).
12. The point of reflection should appear at (4, 7).
13. The point of reflection should appear at (7, -2).
14. The point of reflection should appear at (-1,2).
15. The point of reflection should appear at (-7, -3).

ANSWER SHEET

4.1B Congruent Figures

1. Rotation. Explanation: The rectangle is rotated 180 degrees around the origin.
2. Translation. Explanation: The rectangle was moved down 4 units and over 5 units.
3. Reflection. Explanation: The triangle is reflected across x = 1.
4. Translation. Explanation: The triangle was moved down 6 and left 1.
5. Rotation. Explanation: The triangle is rotated 270 degrees around the origin.
6. C. Explanation: When rotated 180 degrees, the sides line up.
7. C. Explanation: When rotated 180 degrees, the sides line up.
8. A. Explanation: When rotated 180 degrees, the sides line up.
9. 5 units to the right and 2 units down. Explanation: Compare Point A on the pre-image to Point A on the image. (6, 7) and (-1, 5)
10. 8 units to the left and 6 units down. Explanation: Compare Point A on the pre-image to Point A on the image. For x, 7 - (-1) = 8. For y, 8 - 2 = 6
11. 2 units to the left and 2 units down. Explanation: Compare Point A on the pre-image to Point A on the image. For x, 7 - 5 = 2. For y, 0 - (-2) = 2
12. 2 units to the right. Explanation: Compare Point A on the pre-image to Point A on the image. For x, 2 - 4 = --2. A negative number indicates a shift to the left.
13. A. Explanation: When reflected, these sides are congruent.
14. A. Explanation: When reflected, these sides are congruent.
15. Answers may vary.

4.1.C Transformations on a Coordinate Plane

1. The point should be at (0, 2) because it is twice the distance from the origin as the pre-image.
2. The point should be at (3, 6) because it is three times the distance from the origin as the pre-image.
3. The point should be at (0, 2) because it is a quarter the distance from the origin as the pre-image.
4. The point should be at (0, 3) because it is half the distance from the origin as the pre-image.

5. The point should be at **(3, 0)** because it is three times the distance from the origin as the pre-image.

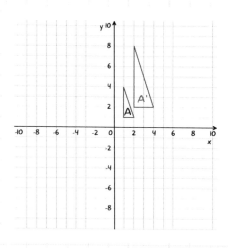

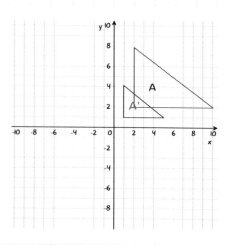

6.

7.

8. C. Explanation: The triangle is rotated **270** degrees about the origin.

9. True. Explanation: (-1, **5**) is the pre-image point (-5, 1) rotated **270** degrees.

10. True. Explanation: (-1, -1) is the pre-image point (-1, 1) rotated **270** degrees.

11. True. Explanation: (-6,-5) is on triangle X and (-5,6) is on triangle A.

12. **3**. Explanation: The image is **3** times larger.

13. $\frac{1}{3}$. Explanation: The image is $\frac{1}{3}$ the size.

14. Answers may vary. Explanation: To get from (1,1) to (3,-2) move three units down and two units to the right.

15. Answers may vary. Explanation: To get from (-4, 0) to (-4, 3) move three units up.

ANSWER SHEET

4.1D Similar Figures

1. No. Explanation: The rectangles have different shapes.
2. Yes. Explanation: The shapes are the same, just scaled.
3. Yes. Explanation: The shapes are the same, just rotated.
4. No. Explanation: The shapes are not the same.
5. Yes. Explanation: The shapes are the same, just rotated.
6. Yes
7. The shapes are the same just translated and rotated.
8. Yes
9. The shapes are the same just scaled.
10. No
11. The shapes are not the same.
12. Yes
13. The shapes are the same just rotated and scaled.
14. Answers may vary.
15. Answers may vary but should use some type of transformation.

4.2.A Intro to Pythagorean Theorem

1. $2^2 + 3^2$. Explanation: The square root of 4 is 2. The square root of 9 is 3.
2. $5^2 + 4^2$. Explanation: The square root of 25 is 5. The square root of 16 is 4.
3. $8^2 + 9^2$. Explanation: The square root of 64 is 8. The square root of 81 is 9.
4. $4^2 + 5^2$. Explanation: The square root of 25 is 5. The square root of 16 is 4.
5. $2^2 + 6^2$. Explanation: The square root of 4 is 2. The square root of 36 is 6.
6. 81 + 100. Explanation: 9 squared is 81. 10 squared is 100.
7. 9 + 100. Explanation: 3 squared is 9. 10 squared is 100.
8. 16 + 36. Explanation: 4 squared is 16. 6 squared is 36.
9. 25 + 64. Explanation: 5 squared is 25. 8 squared is 64.
10. 16 + 9. Explanation: 4 squared is 16. 3 squared is 9.

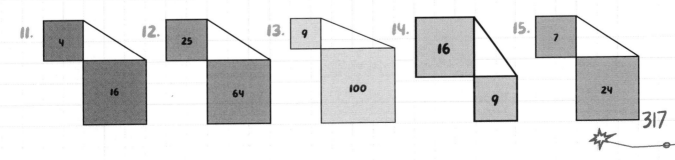

11. 4 / 16 12. 25 / 64 13. 9 / 100 14. 16 / 9 15. 7 / 24

4.2.B Applying the Pythagorean Theorem - Part I

1. 13. Explanation: $12^2 + 5^2 = c^2$
2. 5. Explanation: $4^2 + 3^2 = c^2$
3. 10. Explanation: $8^2 + 6^2 = c^2$
4. 17. Explanation: $8^2 + 15^2 = c^2$
5. 15. Explanation: $9^2 + 12^2 = c^2$
6. 16. Explanation: $a^2 + 12^2 = 20^2$
7. 21. Explanation: $a^2 + 20^2 = 29^2$
8. 18. Explanation: $a^2 + 24^2 = 30^2$
9. 7. Explanation: $a^2 + 24^2 = 25^2$
10. 16. Explanation: $a^2 + 30^2 = 34^2$
11. 15. Explanation: Side B is half the length of 24. $9^2 + 12^2 = c^2$
12. 9. Explanation: Side B is half the length of 24. $a^2 + 12^2 = 15^2$
13. 30. Explanation: Side B is half the length of 36. $24^2 + 18^2 = c^2$
14. 3. Explanation: Side B is half the length of 8. $a^2 + 4^2 = 5^2$
15. 15. Explanation: Side B is half the length of 18. $12^2 + 9^2 = c^2$

4.2.C Applying the Pythagorean Theorem - Part II

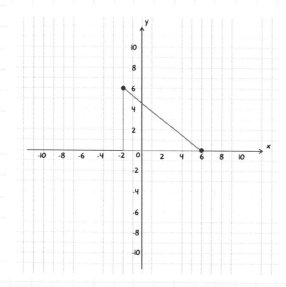

1.

2.   6 and 8. Use the coordinate plane to count the number of units on each side.

3.   10. Explanation: $6^2 + 8^2 = 100$. The square root of 100 is 10.

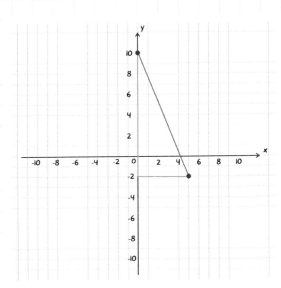

4.

5.   5 and 12. Use the coordinate plane to count the number of units on each side.

6.   13. Explanation: $5^2 + 12^2 = c^2$

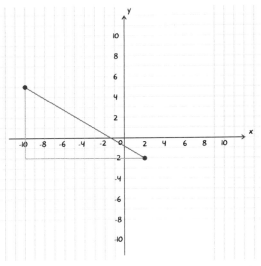

7.

8.   9 and 12. Use the coordinate plane to count the number of units on each side..

9.   15. Explanation: $9^2 + 12^2 = c^2$

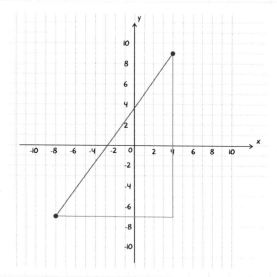

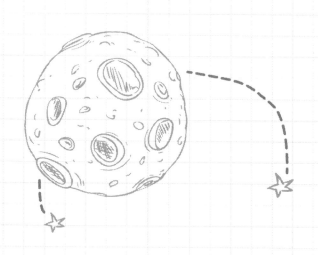

10.

11. 12 and 16. Use the coordinate plane to count the number of units on each side.

12. 20. Explanation: $12^2 + 16^2 = c^2$

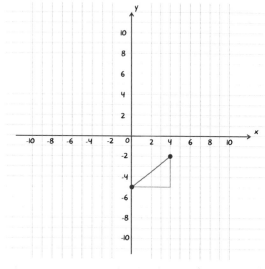

13.

14. 4 and 3. Use the coordinate plane to count the number of units on each side.

15. 5. Explanation: $4^2 + 3^2 = c^2$

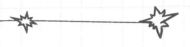

4.3. Volume of Cones, Cylinders and Spheres

1. 8.38. Explanation: $v = (3.14)(2)^2 \left(\dfrac{2}{3}\right)$

2. 2.09. Explanation: $v = (3.14)(1)^2 \left(\dfrac{2}{3}\right)$

3. 3.14. Explanation: $v = (3.14)(1)^2 \left(\dfrac{3}{3}\right)$

4. 12.57. Explanation: $v = (3.14)(2)^2 \left(\dfrac{3}{3}\right)$

5. 20.94. Explanation: $v = (3.14)(2)^2 \left(\dfrac{5}{3}\right)$

6. 9.42. Explanation: $v = (3.14)(1)^2(3)$
7. 37.7. Explanation: $v = (3.14)(2)^2(3)$
8. 21.21. Explanation: $v = (3.14)(1.5)^2(3)$
9. 31.42. Explanation: $v = (3.14)(2)^2(2.5)$
10. 62.83. Explanation: $v = (3.14)(2)^2(5)$
11. 3,053.63. Explanation: $v = \left(\dfrac{4}{3}\right)(3.14)(9)^3$

12. 33.51. Explanation: $v = \left(\dfrac{4}{3}\right)(3.14)(2)^3$

13. 1436.76. Explanation: $v = \left(\dfrac{4}{3}\right)(3.14)(7)^3$

14. 904.78. Explanation: $v = \left(\dfrac{4}{3}\right)(3.14)(6)^3$

15. 65.42. Explanation: $v = \left(\dfrac{4}{3}\right)(3.14)(2.5)^3$

4.4 Chapter Test

1. A. Explanation: The triangle is rotated 90 degrees about the origin.
2. C. Explanation: The rectangle is translated 3 units down and 2 units to the right.
3. B. Explanation: The triangle is reflected across the y-axis.
4. (8,2). Explanation: The point should lie at (8,2) to show reflection across the line.

5.

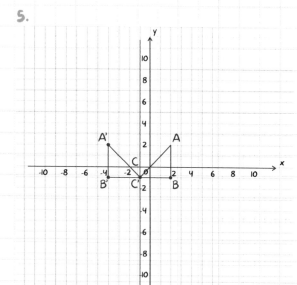

6. **180** degrees. Explanation: The point is rotated two quadrants.

7. **3** units to the left and **5** units down. Explanation: Compare Point A on the pre-image to Point A on the image. For x, 9 - 6 = 3. For y, 10 - 5 = 5. Positive numbers indicated an increase on the number lines.

8. B. Explanation: When rotated, the sides are the same.

9. A. Explanation: When rotated, the sides are the same.

10. **(0, 6)**. Explanation: The point is twice as far from the origin as Point A.

11. **(0, 5)**. Explanation: The point is half the distance from the origin as Point A.

12. Yes.

13. The shapes are the same just scaled and rotated about the origin.

14. **4.19**. Explanation: $v = (3.14)(1)^2 \left(\frac{4}{3}\right)$

15. **14.14**. Explanation: $v = \left(\frac{4}{3}\right)(3.14)(1.5)^3$

16. **14.14**. Explanation: $v = (3.14)(1.5)^2(2)$

17. $3^2 + 7^2$. Explanation: The square root of 9 is 3. The square root of 49 is 7.

18. $4 + 9 = c^2$. Explanation: 2 squared is 4. 3 squared is 9.

19. **3**. Explanation: $4^2 + a^2 = 5^2$. 25 - 16 = 9. The square root of 9 is 3.

20. **10**. Explanation: $6^2 + 8^2 = 100$, The square root of 100 is 10.

ANSWER SHEET

Chapter 5

5.1 A Scatter Plots

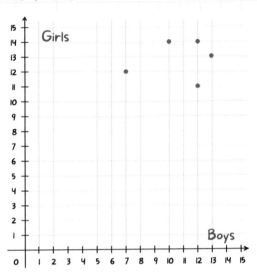

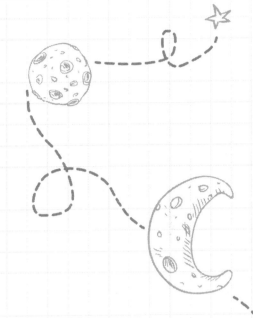

1.
2. There is no clear association between the two variables
3. C. Explanation: There is no association between the number of girls and the number of boys in a class

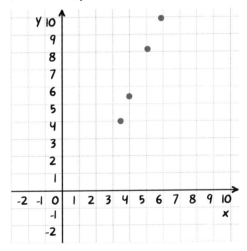

4.
5. The variables appear to have a positive and linear association because the y value increases as the x value increases
6. B. Explanation: As height increases, so does shoe size.

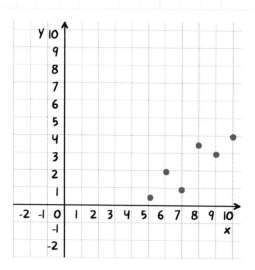

7.

8. The variables seem to have a positive and linear association because in general the y values increase as the x values increase

9. A. Explanation: This is the lowest point on the scatter plot

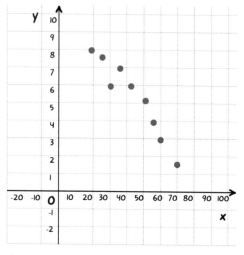

10.

11. The variables appear to have a negative linear association because the y values decrease as the x values increase

12. A. Explanation: As age increases, miles walked tends to decrease.

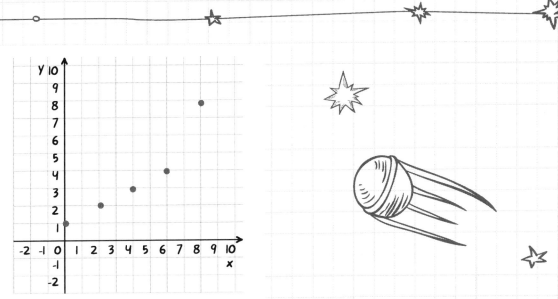

13.

14. The variables appear to have a positive association because the values increase together

15. B. Explanation: At 8 hours of practice there is an outlier (a point away from the rest of the data points).

5.1.B Linear Associations

1. Line m. Line m is close to all of the data points and has the same number of points above it as it does below.

2. Line m. Line m is close to all of the data points and has the same number of points above it as it does below.

3. Line n. Line n is close to all of the data points and has the same number of points above it as it does below.

4. Line l. Line l is close to all of the data points and has the same number of points above it as it does below.

5. Line m. Line m is close to all of the data points and has the same number of points above it as it does below.

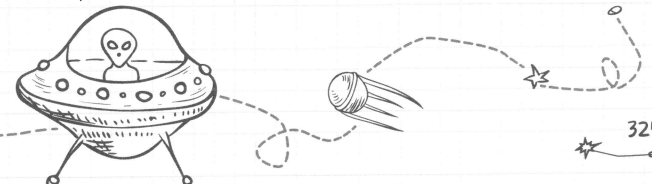

325

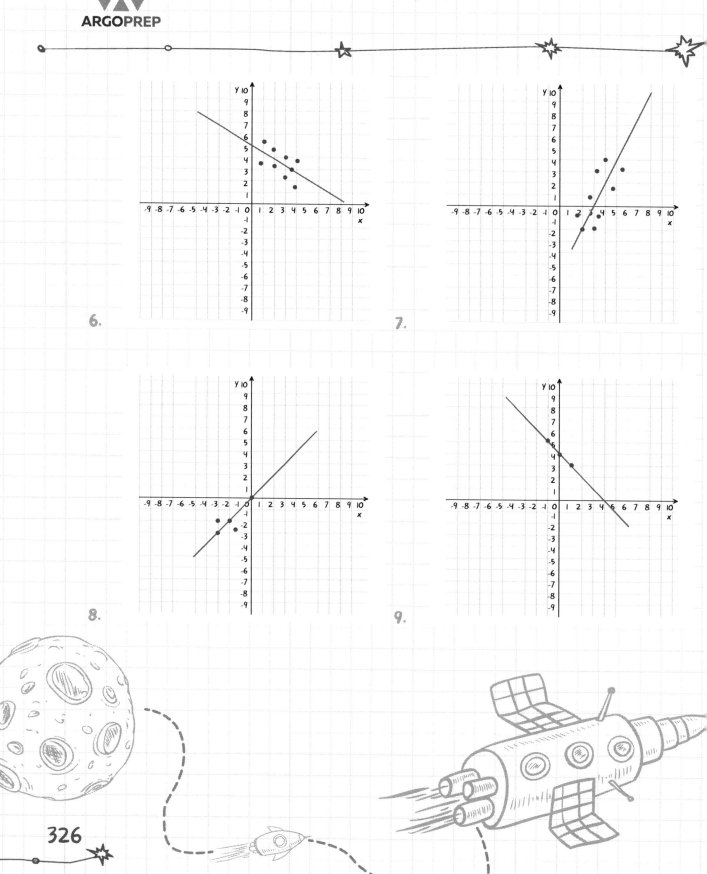

6.

7.

8.

9.

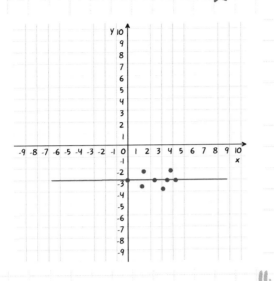

10.

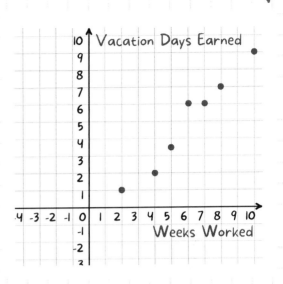

11.

12. A. Explanation: The values increase together.

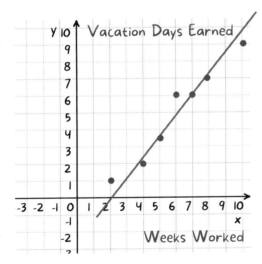

13.

14. A. The point lies at (3, 1).

15. Answers may vary. The line of best fit suggests that you must work at least 3 weeks to earn vacation days, which does not match the data perfectly.

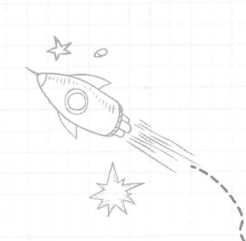

5.1.C Equation of a Linear Model

1. 0. Explanation: When x is zero, y is also zero.

2. $\dfrac{(4-2)}{(2-1)} = 2$

3. $y = 2x$. Explanation: Use slope intercept form ($y = mx + b$).
4. B. Explanation: The slope gives us the rate of change, which is 2 over 1.
5. A. Explanation: Plug 4 in for x. $y = 2(4)$.
6. 7. Explanation: When x is zero, y is 7.

7. $\dfrac{1}{2} \cdot \dfrac{(0-7)}{(4-0)} = \dfrac{2}{4}$

8. $y = \dfrac{1}{2}x + 7$. Explanation: Use slope intercept form ($y = mx + b$).
9. B. Explanation: The time of bed increases as the number of cookies increases.
10. B. Explanation: The rate of change is given by the slope.
11. 6. Explanation: The line crosses the y-axis at 6.

12. $-\dfrac{1}{3} \cdot \dfrac{(5-6)}{(3-0)} = -\dfrac{1}{3}$

13. $y = -\dfrac{1}{3}x + 6$. Explanation: Use slope intercept form ($y = mx + b$).

14. C. Explanation: As the x value increases, the y value decreases.

15. 18 miles. Explanation: Plug in 0 for the y value and solve for x. $y = \left(\dfrac{1}{3}\right)x + 6$

5.1.D Two Way Models

1. 50. Explanation: Add all of the responses (12 + 16 + 14 + 8).
2. 60%. Explanation: 12 + 18 = 30 people out of 50 prefer pink.
3. 25%. Explanation: 18 + 6 = 24 female students. Of those 24, 6 prefer blue. $\dfrac{6}{24}$
4. 20. Explanation: Add the responses for blue (14 + 6 = 20)
5. 26. Explanation: Add the responses for male (12 + 14 = 26)
6. 80. Explanation: Add all of the responses 9 + 23 + 31 + 17

7. 50%. 23 + 17 = 40 out of 80
8. 60%. 31 + 17 = 48 out 80
9. 32. Add the responses under the chocolate row (9 + 23)
10. 40. Explanation: Add the responses under the under 25 column (9 + 31)
11. 25. Explanation: Half of 50 is 25
12. 5. Explanation: 20% of 25 is 5
13. 33%. Explanation: 10 out of 30 is 33%
14. 20. Explanation: (15 + 5 = 20 or 50 total - 30 male = 20 female)

15.

Preference	Male	Female
Chocolate Candy	20	5
Sour Candy	10	15

5.2 Chapter Test

1. B. Explanation: The y values decrease as the x values descrease.
2. A. Explanation: The scatter plot can be represented with a straight line.
3. B. There is one data point far away from the rest of the data points.

4.

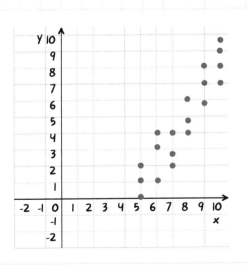

5. Positive Linear Association. Explanation: The values increase together.

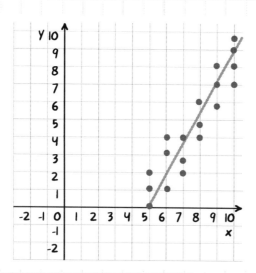

6.

7. C. Explanation: There are no outliers or clusters.

8. Negative Linear Association. Explanation: The y value decreases as the x value increases.

9. 9. Explanation: The line crosses the y axis at 9.

10. $-\dfrac{1}{2}$. Explanation: $\dfrac{(8-9)}{(2-0)} = -\dfrac{1}{2}$

11. $y = -\dfrac{1}{2}x + 9$. Explanation: Use slope intercept form $y = mx + b$.

12. 18. Explanation: Plug in 0 for the y value and solve for x. $y = -\dfrac{1}{2}(x) + 9$

13. A. Every two miles, the gas decreases by one gallon

14. 58.3%. Explanation: 7 + 5 = 12 total moms. 7 out of 12 = .583 x 10 = 58.3

15. 15. Explanation: Add the numbers in the golf row. 10 + 5 = 15

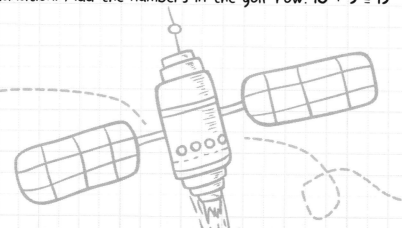

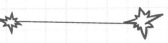
Chapter 6: End of Year Test

1. A. Explanation: -5 can be expressed as a fraction of two integers.
2. A. Explanation: $\frac{6}{2}$ is already expressed as a fraction of two integers.
3. B. Explanation: The decimal continues without repeating and it cannot be expressed as a simple fraction.
4. A. Explanation: $\sqrt{49}$ can be expressed as a fraction of two integers.
5. B. Explanation: The decimal continues without repeating and it cannot be expressed as a fraction of two integers.
6. B. Explanation: The decimal continues without repeating and it cannot be expressed as a fraction of two integers.
7. A. Explanation: $\frac{7}{2}$ is be expressed as a fraction of two integers.
8. B. Explanation: The decimal continues without repeating and it cannot be expressed as a fraction of two integers.
9. A. Explanation: The number can be expressed as a fraction of two integers.
10. A. Explanation: The number can be expressed as a fraction of two integers.
11. 9, $\sqrt{90}$, 10, 11.
12. -5, 7, $\sqrt{54}$, 10.
13. $\sqrt{5}$, 3, 4.
14. <. Explanation: $7 \times 7 = 49$. Therefore, we know $\sqrt{40}$ is less than 7.
15. >. Explanation: $6 \times 6 = 36$. Therefore, we know it is greater than $\sqrt{30}$.
16. =. Explanation: The square root of 64 is 8.
17. Answers may vary. Explanation: Should show an understanding that $2\pi - 5$ is between 1 and 2.
18. Answers may vary. Explanation: Should show an understanding that $\sqrt{124}$ is between 11 and 12.

19.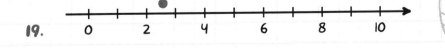

20.

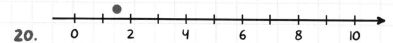

21. A. Explanation: The decimal shifts 9 places to the right.

22. B. Explanation: The decimal shifts one place to the right.

23. 2.0×10^7 which translates to **20,000,000**.

$\underline{1.2 \times 10^9}$

6.0×10^1

24. 1.65×10^4

$8,000 + 8,500 = 16,500$

25. 3.0×10^{-1}

$.25 + .05 = .30$

26. 1.0×10^4

$17,500 - 7,500 = 10,000$

27. 4.0×10^3

$4,525 - 525 = 4,000$

28. C. Explanation: Both of the equations are equal once simplified.

29. C. Explanation: Both of the equations are equal once simplified.

30. A. Explanation: The variables do not cancel out.

31. No. Explanation: There is more than one y-value when x is equal to **-8**

32. Yes. Explanation: Each input (x-value) only has one output (y-value).

33. B. Explanation: The input 1 (x-value) has more than one output (y-value).

34. B. Explanation: The input 1 (x-value) has more than one output (y-value).

35. B. Explanation: The input 0 (x-value) has more than one output (y-value).

36. A. Explanation: The input -1 (x-value) has more than one output (y-value) for table B making it not a function.

37. B. Explanation: The slope (**3**) remains constant.

38. A. Explanation: The slope $\left(\dfrac{1}{10}\right)$ remains constant.

39. B. Explanation: Representation a has a slope of $\dfrac{1}{2}$. Representation b has a slope of 10 (y = 10x + 5).

40. B. Representation a intercepts the y axis between 3 and 4. Representation b intercepts at 5.

41. y = 2x -4. Explanation: Slope is 2. y-intercept is -4.

42. y = $\dfrac{1}{4}$x -1. Explanation: Slope is $\dfrac{1}{4}$. y-intercept is -1.

43. $y = 2x - 1$. Explanation: Slope is **2**. y-intercept is -1.

44. $y = x + 7$. Explanation: Slope is 1. y-intercept is 7.

45. $y = 4x + 2$. Explanation: Slope is 4. y-intercept is 2.

46. $y = \frac{1}{5}x - 2$. Explanation: Slope is $\frac{1}{5}$. y-intercept is -2.

47. B. Explanation: The function representing Josh is higher.

48. C. Explanation: The functions intersect when $x=8$.

49. B. Explanation: Look at the values of y for each runner when $x = 5$.

50. C. Explanation: Brant's y values are greater than Josh's after mile 8.

51. A.

52. C.

53. B.

54. (-2, 4).

55. The line of reflection is draw at $x = -2$.

56. 180 degrees.

57. 4 to the left and 5 up.

58. B.

59. C.

60. (0, -4). Explanation: The image is twice the distance from the origin.

61. (0, 1). Explanation: The point is half the distance from the origin.

62. The shapes are similar.

63. They are the same shape just scaled.

64. **58.64**. Explanation: $\pi r^2 \left(\dfrac{14}{3}\right)$

65. 179.59. Explanation: $\left(\dfrac{4}{3}\right) \pi \left(3.5\right)^3$

66. 603.19. Explanation: $\pi \left(4\right)^2 \left(12\right)$

67. $4^2 + 10^2 = c^2$. Explanation: The square of 16 is 4. The square of 100 is 10.

68. $144 + 16 = c^2$. Explanation: 12 squared is 144. 4 squared is 16.

69. 5. Explanation: Side b is half the size of 24. So $a^2 + 12^2 = 13^2$

70. 17. Explanation: Draw a right triangle. Then count the number of units on each side. Then solve for c: $8^2 + 15^2 = c^2$

71. A. Explanation: The y values decrease as the x values increase.

72. B. Explanation: The x and y values increase together.

73. A. Explanation: The model could be represented with a straight line.

74. B. Explanation: The model could not be represented with a straight line.

75. B. Explanation: The data points are all close together.

76. A. Explanation: One data point is farther away from the rest.

77. Positive. Explanation: The y value increases as the x values increase.

78.

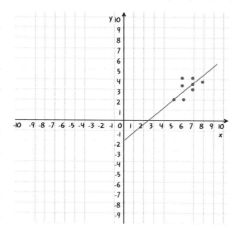

79. C. Explanation: There are no outliers or clusters.

80. Answers may vary.

81. Negative, Linear Association. Explanation: It can be represented with a straight line. As one value increases, the other decreases.

82. 10

83. $-\frac{7}{4}$. You can use the points (0, 10) and (4, 3) to calculate the slope.

84. $y = -\frac{7}{4}x + 10$

85. B.

86. A.

87. 100. Explanation: Add all of the responses (22 + 24 + 31 + 23)

88. 53. Explanation: 22 + 31.

89. 47. Explanation: 24 + 23

ANSWER SHEET

90. **41.5%.** Explanation: **22** out of **53** males preferred swimming. $\frac{22}{53}$ = .415 x 10

91. **58.5%.** Explanation: **31** out of **53** males preferred basketball. $\frac{31}{53}$ = .5849 x 10

92. **48.9%.** Explanation: $\frac{23}{47}$ = .489 x 10

93. **51.1%.** Explanation: $\frac{24}{47}$ = .510 x 10

94. **40.** Explanation: Add all of the values.
95. **20.** Explanation: 17 + 3
96. **20.** Explanation: 15 + 5
97. **8.** Explanation: 15 − 7
98. **18.** Explanation: 5 + 13
99. **22.** Explanation: 15 + 7
100. **65%.** Explanation: 13 out of 20 is .65 times 10 is 65%.

Made in the USA
Middletown, DE
16 April 2020